F

the Way to Timbuktu

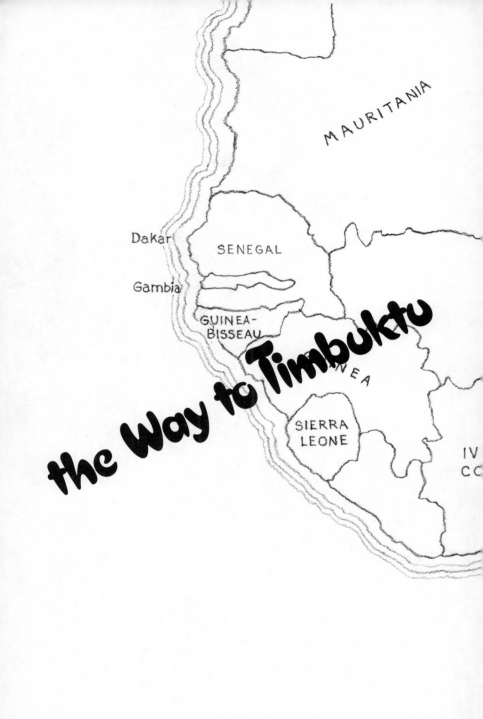

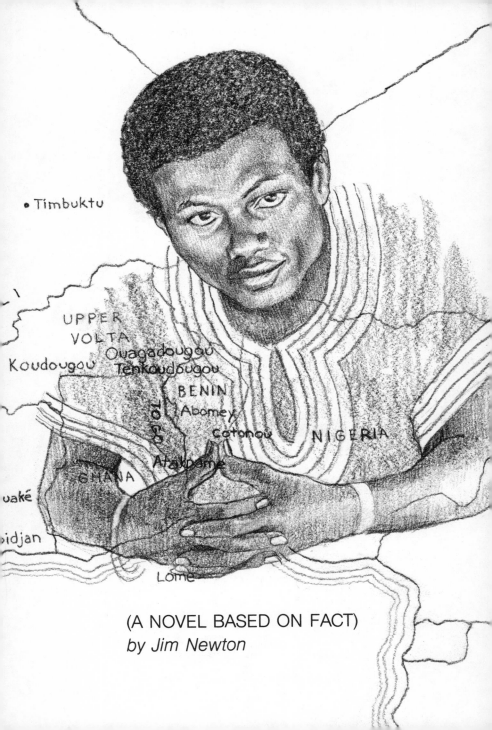

Timbuktu

UPPER
VOLTA
Ouagadougou
Koudougou Tenkoudougou

BENIN
Abomey
Cotonou NIGERIA
Atakpame
GHANA
uaké
idjan
Lomé

(A NOVEL BASED ON FACT)
by Jim Newton

A Publication of the

**FOREIGN MISSION BOARD
SOUTHERN BAPTIST CONVENTION**

© Copyright 1981 ● CONVENTION PRESS
All rights reserved
Nashville, Tennessee

5136-17

Photos by Foreign Mission Board

This book is the text for a course
in the subject area *Missions* of the
Church Study Course

Dewey Decimal Classification F
Subject Heading: Missions—Africa—Fiction

Printed in the United States of America

TABLE OF CONTENTS

part one

1. Nightmare of Death 8
2. Quest for Understanding 21
3. The Center of His Will 38
4. Desire for Knowledge 48
5. Educational Confrontation 59
6. Clearing the Way 68

Decision in Dakar

part two

7. Journey to Abidjan 80
8. Preaching in Love 99
9. A Second Love 113
10. Crisis in Koudougou 120
11. Love Finds a Way 131

Love in Lomé

part three

12. The Road to Gomé 148
13. The Curse of Vodu 163
14. Appointment in Abomey 185
15. Confrontation in Cotonou 201
16. Finding the Way 207

Beginning in Benin

About the Author 215

Pronunciation of Significant Words

Part One 216
Part Two 216
Part Three 217

part one

Decision in Dakar

NIGHTMARE OF DEATH

A *I*
*SOFT MOAN SILENCED THE
CHIRP of the cricket hiding in a
dark corner of the small,*
crowded room in Dakar, Senegal, West
Africa. For several moments there was
no sound. Then the cricket began its
"chirp-chirp, chirp-chirp" again, slowly
at first, then rapidly. A moan silenced
the cricket once more.

The moonlight shining through the
open window of the room revealed a
young African man tossing on his sleeping mat on the floor. Silence again.
Then slowly, carefully, the cricket again
began his monotonous song.

"Ayiiiiii!" A loud scream pierced the
cool night air. The short young man
bolted upright from his sleeping mat,
and the cricket jumped high to a darker
corner. A second scream filled the
silence of the night.

A young man in downtown Dakar, Senegal

A few seconds later, the curtain hanging over the door to the adjacent room swished open, and a muscular man in his forties rushed to the young man's side.

"What is it, my son?" the older man asked anxiously.

"It's the dream again," was the reply. "It's always the same. But tonight it was worse."

"Tell me about it, Amasou," the older man said, using his son's tribal name rather than his French name, Jean-Marc. "You must talk about it. Talking about your dream will help get it out of your mind."

"I dreamed I saw him die again," Jean-Marc murmured. "Oh, father, it was terrible. It was so real. Pierre and I were walking to classes at the *lycée,* and I was teasing him about the Wolof girl he had met the week before. As usual, we took the shortcut through the construction zone where they are building the skyscraper. I wasn't paying much attention, but Pierre heard the warning cry from above. He suddenly shoved me hard, and I fell to the ground just off the pathway. The split second that followed seemed like minutes, even longer this time. Then there was Pierre lying on the very spot where I had been standing. The steel girder that fell from the crane overhead had hit him on the head.

"The sight was awful, but the dream is even worse. Blood spurted through the air, but Pierre didn't make a sound as he fell. I got up and cradled his bleeding head in my lap. He tried to speak. At first the words wouldn't come. Finally, he managed to whisper: 'Promise you will take the gospel to our people. They have never heard the good news.' Then, without a whimper, he died in my arms while I screamed for help."

Zukono put his strong arms around his distraught son, trying to comfort him. Jean-Marc began to weep softly, even though he did not want to show his emotion in front of his father. His father, who lived by the traditions of the Fon, did not approve of a man shedding tears. The Fon are strong, proud people with a rich heritage.

Suppressing his tears, Jean-Marc walked to the window and looked into the moonlit courtyard outside their two-room apartment. For several moments he was silent. Then he blurted out what was really troubling him deep down inside.

"But why did *he* have to die? Why was it Pierre instead of me? If he hadn't pushed me, I would have been killed, not Pierre. I'd rather be dead than for my best friend to have died saving my life."

Zukono walked to his son's side and stared out into the darkness. "It was your *fa,* your destiny," he replied. "You must not doubt it; you must only accept it."

"But the dream comes every night, haunting me, tormenting me," Jean-Marc said. "I can't sleep. I don't even want to eat. And I can't study."

Staring into the courtyard, Zukono suggested that they go outside to talk. "It's almost four o'clock in the morning, and there's not much use going back to bed. I need to be up by 5:00 to get ready to go to work. Let's sit under the tree in the compound so we can talk without disturbing Narie and the children."

Zukono didn't say so, but he didn't want to wake up his wife and the younger children. It was best not to involve Narie because she had become irritable lately, and the two were constantly arguing. Besides, she didn't understand Fon, and he and Amasou could best communicate in their own tribal language.

II

Outside, the cool harmattan wind was blowing, sweeping sand and dust from the Sahara into Dakar like a giant billow. The wind came every December, sometimes howling and blowing with terrible force. At night the temperature often dropped as low as 60 degrees. In Dakar, that was cold compared to the sweltering heat of the daytime.

Zukono and Jean-Marc walked silently to the huge baobab tree, sat down, and leaned against its 20-foot-wide trunk. Jean-Marc looked at his father in the pale light. Zukono's muscular neck and firm face reflected the physical strength of a blacksmith, the trade followed by the men of his family.

Jean-Marc was silent, pensive. Actually, he preferred not to

A baobab tree in Dakar, Senegal

talk. He wanted to pray, to get some answer from God. Since his best friend's tragic death, Jean-Marc had found it hard to pray. He didn't know why. But it was something he could not talk to his father about because his father was not a believer.

Zukono broke the silence. "My son, I want to tell you what I think is causing these nightmares."

Even before his father started, Jean-Marc knew what would be said and dreaded the argument that was likely to follow. He had heard it all before.

Picking up a small stick and swirling it in the dust, Zukono said he regretted that there was no longer a *voduno* (chief priest or diviner) living in Dakar to interpret the meaning of the dream.

"If only old Anagonu had not died three years ago," Zukono lamented. "He was the only Fon *voduno* from Dahomey in Dakar."

Zukono consistently refused to use the word Benin, the name of his homeland since 1975, when the name of the country was changed. Zukono would always think of his homeland as the Kingdom of Dahomey.

"I am not a *voduno*, and I do not know the secret of casting the palm nuts to interpret the meaning of dreams, but I will tell you what I think your dream means," Zukono said.

"The spirit of your *xonto daxo* (best friend) is coming back to haunt you because you did not fulfill your responsibilities as 'best friend' and 'blood brother' at Bakari's funeral. You may call him 'Pierre,' but he was Sonni Bakari and you were Amasou then. You are still, as far as I am concerned."

"But, father," interrupted Jean-Marc, "when Pierre and I became Christians, we put aside those tribal customs based on superstitions. I know you still believe in them, but I don't, and neither did Pierre."

"It makes no difference what you believe now," snapped Zukono. "The power of the *vodu* (god) is stronger than your white man's God. You and Bakari 'drank the *vodun*' together when you were 12 years old. You made a blood pact with each other, vowing to be 'best friends' and 'blood brothers' for life, and even unto death."

Standing to emphasize his point, Zukono turned to face Jean-Marc, staring deeply into his troubled eyes. Towering over his son, who remained seated under the baobab tree, Zukono raised his voice and launched into a diatribe:

"I warned you about the responsibilities then, but you insisted. Sonni Bakari was not worthy to be your best friend because he was not Fon. He was from another tribe and another country. Still you insisted on making the blood pact, even after old Anagonu warned you that if you or Bakari ever died, the survivor was obligated to fulfill all the vows of the rites of burial according to the Fon custom. You have not done that."

Jean-Marc recalled watching Anagonu prepare the drink of

kola nuts, chicken, chicken blood, and other secret ingredients. He remembered the excitement he and Pierre had felt.

Standing up to face Zukono, he said: "But, father, we were only kids. It really didn't mean anything to us. It was just something fun to do. From my youngest days, you had told me about the Fon custom for young boys to make a 'blood brother' pact with their very best friend, and Pierre was my best friend. At the time it seemed like a good thing to do. But after we became Christians two years ago, we stopped taking the custom seriously. I just don't believe any of that voodoo magic now."

Zukono's lips tightened, and his eyes pierced Jean-Marc's like steel arrows. He resumed his sermon: "You can scoff and refuse to believe if you want to, but there is power in the *vodun*. I, too, drank the *vodun* with my best friend. We drank the *vodun* when we were 12 years old, as you did. But I carried out the vows I made when my blood brother was killed.

"When Bakari was killed last month, I told you what you should do, but you would not listen. You did not wash Bakari's body and shave all his hair according to our customs. You did not shave your own head. Or clip Bakari's finger and toe nails."

Zukono's voice rose. He seemed almost unaware of Jean-Marc as he began a vivid recital of each step of the ritual. "You did not keep the death watch to prevent anyone from stealing Bakari's clothing, hair, or nail clippings—things that might be used to make a fetish. You did not sing the ritual song and gird Bakari's loins with the burial loin cloth—or dance the *monogbogo* when his body was buried. You did not bring gifts of soap, a sponge, a small water pot, mats, a pipe, a pair of pants, a shirt, a cap, and a drink prescribed by custom. You did not cover his body with a cloth with 16 stripes."

He stopped abruptly and glared at Jean-Marc. "You did not, and you are not, observing three months of mourning by wearing only black or indigo blue. Because of this the spirit of Bakari has come back to haunt you, Amasou! You may be a

Christian now, but you still have responsibility to fulfll those vows. It is the spirit of Bakari that is causing your nightmares!"

Jean-Marc knew what was coming next. Zukono believed that although the dead and all supernatural beings can be reasoned with, when their patience is at an end, they seek to punish the living. He believed sacrifices and proper messages must be sent through a chief priest to appease the spirit of the dead.

"We must find a Fon *voduno* who will create a fetish to protect you from harm. Otherwise, you will not only have nightmares; you may die," Zukono said.

"Oh, father, I just don't believe all that voodoo superstition. And neither did Pierre. I don't know why I am having these nightmares, but I do know Pierre's spirit is not haunting me.

"Pierre and I were more than best friends and blood brothers. We were brothers in Christ. We were 'blood brothers' because our sins have been cleansed by the blood of Jesus Christ shed on the cross. And Pierre's spirit is with God in heaven today—not here on earth 'haunting' me."

III

By this time both Jean-Marc and Zukono were almost shouting, and their voices reverberated off the hard clay walls of the compound. Zukono's wife Narie, a big woman who towered over Jean-Marc, came out and scolded her husband and stepson.

"Quiet, you two! You'll wake the whole neighborhood!" she commanded in Wolof, the language spoken in the home. She was Peul, one of the nomadic Fulani tribes from western Senegal, but neither Zukono nor Jean-Marc spoke her tribal language. Instead, they all communicated in Wolof, the most common African language in Dakar, and sometimes in French, the official language of the government. But Narie, as was true of the women of her culture, had little formal education. She had difficulty with French.

Zukono stood to his full height, which was only an inch

taller than his wife's, and reprimanded her for interrupting.
"Go back inside," he commanded. "This is a matter only between Amasou and me. And make us some breakfast. It's
almost time for everyone to get up anyway."

Narie glared at her husband for a few moments and then
turned to obey. She knew what would happen if she did not.
Zukono was a strong man, and sometimes he beat her when
he was angry. She could tell that whatever he and Jean-Marc
were discussing had upset him terribly. She went inside, and
grumbling and muttering under her breath, began to mix
two bowls of porridge made with the flour of guinea corn.

Outside, Jean-Marc ambled over to the well in the center of
the compound, leaning against the three-foot-high circular
clay wall that surrounded the well. He decided to use the
silent treatment with his father, knowing it did not do any
good to argue with the older man. He wanted to tell his father
how faith in God had sustained him throughout the ordeal of
the nightmares that followed his best friend's death, but he
knew his father would not understand.

He could not let his father know about his doubts and the
gnawing question that ached inside him—why God had let
this happen to Pierre so soon after Pierre had felt that God
was calling him to be a pastor. Pierre planned to return to
Timbuktu to share the good news of the gospel with his people. Why did God allow Pierre to die before he had carried out
his calling to be a missionary?

Jean-Marc kept silent about his doubts, for he and Pierre
had never told *anyone* what Pierre felt God was calling him
to be. Pierre had been a Muslim before he accepted Christ;
and although he was never a devout Muslim, he knew his
family back home in Timbuktu would disown him if they
knew he had converted to Christianity. Pierre was worried
when he learned Jean-Marc had told Zukono that both had
accepted Christ. He feared Zukono would tell Sunni, who
lived down the street. Pierre knew that if his uncle found out
he had become a Christian, he would not allow him to live in
his home and would send him back to Timbuktu before he
completed his education. Fortunately, however, Zukono had

never liked Pierre's uncle, Sunni, and had little to do with him.

Deep in his thoughts, Jean-Marc sat on the edge of the well, listening to the sounds of dawn. Zukono, too, was quiet for awhile after the argument and the interruption by his wife. He couldn't understand why he could not pound some sense into his son's head, the way he shaped and molded red-hot iron with his hammer and anvil. He couldn't understand why his son had rejected the gods of his forefathers.

Slowly Zukono turned and walked to the well. Speaking softly to Jean-Marc, he said: "Son, why have you done this to me? Why have you rejected the ways of our people and the gods of our forefathers? Why have you followed after the ways of the *toubob* (white men), and accepted their white God? What's wrong with you? Aren't the gods of our people good enough for you?"

IV

Jean-Marc was silent for several minutes. He didn't want to start another argument. But he sensed in his father's questions a searching, plaintive note. It was almost as if his father wondered if there were more meaning to Jean-Marc's faith in God than Zukono had found in the tribal religion.

Suddenly Jean-Marc remembered reading in the Bible the story of Paul's sermon to the Greeks at the Acropolis in Athens, and he decided to respond to his father's question the way Paul did to the Athenians.

"Father, I will tell you what I believe," he responded carefully. "You and I believe in the same God, but we call him by different names. You and all the Fon people call God by the name 'Mawu.' You believe that Mawu, the creator, is so great that she cannot be troubled with the problems of the people on earth. So the twin gods, Mawu, also goddess of the moon, and Lisa, the god of the sun, had many children. These the Fon people worship as lesser gods, each with its own cult of followers. I've heard you speak so often of the gods called Sagbata, Sogbo, Agbe, Dan, Gou, Agé, and on and on. I know that our family worships Gou, the god of iron, because you and all of your forefathers were blacksmiths. I know you believe that Gou is the god of war because it is through him that the Fon warrior's weapons are effective. I know that you have tried to worship God by making sacrifice to Gou and using fetishes made by the chief priest of Gou.

"But, father, I have found the true God, the true creator. His name is not Mawu, but his name is Jehovah. And our people are partly right when they believe that man cannot truly understand the nature of so great a God who could create the earth and the entire universe. That's why God sent his only Son, Jesus, to live on the earth as a human being, just like you and me. But Jesus was different from the rest of humanity. He lived a perfect life—without sin or disobedience of God's laws—whereas all others have sinned.

"Almost two thousand years ago, to the northeast in the land called Judea, Jesus went about healing the sick, raising the dead, sharing God's love with the outcasts, and showing by his life what God is really like. Through Jesus we know that God really loves us. He cares about you and me personally. Yet, even though Jesus came to help people understand that God is love, he was rejected and crucified on a cruel cross.

"But Jesus rose from the dead three days after he was buried. He appeared to his followers and assured them God would send his Holy Spirit to comfort them always. Now Jesus is in a place called heaven, where those like Pierre who believe in him as Savior from their sin will go after death. Father, I know Pierre is with God the Father and Jesus the Son, even as the Holy Spirit is here with us now in this compound.

"Father, the gods of our people are not good enough for us. The reason our people have so many different gods is that deep down we know that none of them is adequate. But Jesus is more than adequate. He is the true way to know God."

Never once during the entire sermon, although Jean-Marc would never have called it that, did he raise his voice. He spoke calmly, carefully, trying to state clearly what he believed and how it compared to the religion of the Fon people. He tried everything he could to keep his father from reacting with anger.

But he failed. At first, Zukono listened with interest, really wanting to understand why his son had become a Christian. But when Jean-Marc said Fon gods were not good enough, Zukono lost his temper. He was furious.

"You are wrong, Amasou!" he shouted. "The gods of our people are good enough for me, and for you. They have been good enough for a thousand years. They were good enough for my father, my grandfather, and their fathers and grandfathers. We have always worshipped Gou.

"You, however, have rejected the ways of our fathers, even though the *vodun* blessed you. You were born a twin, and twins are a special blessing for our people. But the *vodun* cursed me when your mother and your twin brother died. The fetish priest cursed me, blaming my seed for her death. Remember, our people have always believed that death in childbirth is the most horrible, unspeakable kind of death, and the fetish priest blamed my bad seed for her death. Because of this, no other Fon woman would marry me. They all feared that the curse of death in childbirth would come to them. I am cursed, but you are blessed, Amasou. Even your name has significance, for it means, 'firstborn twin.'

"You should appreciate who you are and the sacrifices I have made for you. For five years after your mother died, I worked in our village of Gomé, trying to find a wife and trying to earn enough money to go somewhere else to start a new life for you. When no Fon woman from our area would marry me, I left Dahomey and brought you here to Dakar to live with my uncle Iosu. We were fortunate that he was still alive then and that we had a place to come. My whole purpose in life in this foreign land has been to earn enough money to give you an education so that you can return one day to our homeland and become a respected government leader. You are blessed by the *vodun*, Amasou, but you don't even appreciate all that I and the gods have done for you."

V

As the sun began to rise in the east, Jean-Marc sat silently on the side of the well, knowing there was no use arguing with his father. Zukono might never understand. Yet, Jean-Marc felt compelled to continue seeking reconciliation. Quietly but firmly he responded; "Father, I do appreciate the sacrifices you have made for my education. I'm trying hard to prepare for the baccalaureate exam. But even if I pass it and am admitted to the university, I don't think I want to be a government worker back in Benin because that government is Marxist. I'm not sure my Christian convictions would allow me to work there."

Zukono's chin dropped to his chest, a look of disappointment covering his strong, angular features. For 14 years he had dreamed and worked for the day his son could complete a degree at the famed University of Dakar and return in triumph to Benin as a government worker. He had believed that success for a Fon was to be a high-ranking government official. That was possible only with a university degree. Now that his son was saying he did not want to be a government worker, all that Zukono had worked for seemed to be vanishing in a puff of smoke.

"My son, I regret the day that you and Bakari accepted this Jesus, the white God of the *toubob*. It has driven a wedge between us and caused you to reject the faith and customs of our forefathers. Worst of all, it seems I have worked all these years for naught. When you accepted the white man's God, you set into action a chain of events that will change all our lives. Nothing could hurt me more."

Sad and dejected, Zukono turned to walk toward the house to eat his porridge and get ready for his job at the nail factory. There was no use talking. He realized he would not change Jean-Marc's mind, and there was nothing Jean-Marc could say that would change his.

Jean-Marc sat staring off into space, dangling his legs on the side of the well. He wasn't hungry. He couldn't eat. He was too troubled in the depths of his soul.

While Zukono and Narie and the three other children ate,

Jean-Marc left. He had to go somewhere to be alone, to think, to find a solution to the problems he knew he would face in the future.

QUEST FOR UNDERSTANDING

I

Jean-Marc opened the gate of the compound and walked out into the unnamed sandy alley that was too narrow to be called a street. As he walked toward the bus stop at *Avenue de la Liberté,* the deep layers of sand in the alley seemed to suck his sandals from his feet. Few cars could drive on the thick sand without getting stuck, but there was little reason for cars to drive down the alley. No one in the entire neighborhood owned a car because no one could afford the 8.7 million West African francs (about $18,000) cost of a car, or the 198 francs-per-liter (about $3.50 per gallon) cost of gasoline.

As Jean-Marc stood waiting for the bus, sounds of the morning filled the air. From the huge loudspeaker on the minaret atop the green-domed Liberté mosque came the plaintive wail of the muezzin as he called the Muslim people to the mosque for morning prayers. It was dawn, and the city was coming to life.

Trucks and carts loaded with vegetables and goods the villagers were taking to market filled the streets. The smell of fish, the primary food of the people, already permeated the air. Taxi horns sounded as the driver swerved in and out to avoid the logjam of people.

Jean-Marc had to scramble fast to board the bus when it ar-

People walking to bus in Dakar, Senegal

rived. There were no seats available, and he was lucky even
to get a place to stand. As usual, Jean-Marc rode the bus
toward the *lycée,* the French-system school that is the equiv-
alent of a high school and junior college in the American
system. But Jean-Marc was in no mood to go to classes. He
was too troubled to study, or even to talk. He wanted to be
alone.

When the bus stopped at his normal departure point, Jean-
Marc stayed aboard. His fare was paid; so, he decided just to
ride aimlessly until he wanted to get off.

Soon the bus turned up the *Route de la Corniche* and
headed toward the University of Dakar. As it passed along the
palm-studded beaches, Jean-Marc decided to get off at a
beautiful park. He walked beneath the palms, out onto the
beach. Taking off his sandals, he let the warm sand seep between his toes, soothing his feet and calming his spirit.

As he walked along the beach away from the sounds of the
city, Jean-Marc was alone with his thoughts. Again, the

haunting anxiety troubled his soul. Why was Pierre the one to die? Was it really meant for that steel beam to hit him instead of Pierre? Why did the girder fall in the first place? Who was responsible for Pierre's death? Did some workman on the construction site fail to secure the huge hook on the cable the crane was using to haul the steel beam to the top of the building? Was it really God's will for Pierre to die? Why Pierre? Why? Why? Why?

Questions. Only questions. Why no answers? Why was God silent? Why couldn't Jean-Marc pray? Why couldn't he feel God's presence the way he had when Pierre was alive, when they had prayed together so many times? If only he could turn back the calendar two months and relive that fateful day in October.

Jean-Marc walked to a coconut palm on the sandy beach and sat down. He stared at the waves pounding the beach, but the haze was so thick that morning that he could hardly see the horizon. Even the harmattan winds did not blow away the haze. He listened to the roar of the waves crashing against the sandy beach. The sound had a soothing, calming

*Panoramic view of Senegal coastline and beach,
Dakar, Senegal*

effect. There were no answers to his troubling questions, but an inexplainable peace seemed to settle over him.

Memories of the good times he and Pierre spent together flashed through his mind. He remembered when they first met as six-year-old boys. Bakari (he had no French name then) was living with his uncle down the alley, having just come to Dakar from a faraway city in Mali called Timbuktu. He was the firstborn son of a slipper maker. His uncle, Sunni, owned a slipper shop in Dakar where he sold the sandals and slippers made by Bakari's father and other merchants in Timbuktu.

The two boys met in the sandy alley that connected their compounds. Seeing Pierre sitting in the sand piling huge mounds of sand over his feet and legs, Jean-Marc went over to play with him. As they joked and played, Pierre lay back in the sand and Jean-Marc completely covered his body with a pile of sand, leaving only his head sticking in the air. The boys got in trouble that day with Sunni's wife for getting Pierre's clothes full of sand.

From that day forward, the two boys were best friends. Jean-Marc had lived in Dakar less than a year and had just begun to learn the Wolof language spoken by most of the people in the *quartier* (neighborhood or quarter) where they lived. Pierre, too, spoke some Wolof; and together they learned that language well, although they usually spoke their tribal languages at home.

Three years after arriving in Dakar to live, Zukono married Narie. They rented the small, two-room apartment in the compound adjacent to Iosu's. Pierre and Jean-Marc were so glad that Zukono chose to remain close to his uncle's compound instead of moving to another *quartier* after his marriage.

As Jean-Marc sat under the palm tree on the beach remembering the past, dozens of incidents he shared with his best friend came to mind. Recalling the time they "drank the *vodun*" to seal their pact to be "best friends" and "blood brothers" for life, Jean-Marc shuddered and quickly tried to think of something else. Jean-Marc didn't want to think about the "blood brother" pact because of the painful memory of the argument with his father that morning.

Other thoughts about his past life with Pierre flashed through Jean-Marc's mind. He recalled the first time they drank too much beer together and how sick they had been. He remembered their early escapades with a neighborhood girl. Shame and remorse flooded his soul when he thought of his life before he and Pierre accepted Christ. He had done so many things he now knew were wrong. But then, they seemed natural—things normal African young men did.

The shame of those memories subsided as Jean-Marc recalled how he and Pierre had become brothers in Christ. It was not a dramatic story, nothing at all like the intrigue of "drinking the *vodun*" together. But a quiet excitement flooded Jean-Marc's mind as he thought of the way he and his best friend came to know Jesus as their best friend.

II

By the time they were 17 years of age, Jean-Marc and Pierre had talked a great deal about the differences between the Muslim religion of Pierre's people and the religion of Jean-Marc's family. Both agreed on one thing—that the religion of their families meant almost nothing to them personally. To Pierre, the religion of Islam seemed nothing but following a meaningless set of rules. His uncle and his father went through the form of praying five times a day and going to the mosque, especially on Friday. But Pierre was unaware of any effect their religion had on them.

For Jean-Marc, the religious beliefs of the Fon meant even less. While there were hundreds of Muslim mosques in Dakar, there were no temples to the Fon god Gou that his father worshipped. Although the tribal religion meant something to Zukono, it was meaningless for Jean-Marc. There were few Fon in Dakar, and his exposure to Fon religious practices was limited. Neither did the Muslim religion practiced by almost 90 percent of the people in Dakar mean anything to him.

Pierre and Jean-Marc did believe there was a god who created the earth, the moon, and the universe. Because Senegal was once a French colony, there were many Catholics in Dakar, and several of their teachers at the school were Catholics. Jean-Marc and Pierre secretly went to Catholic mass several times together, but they didn't understand the meaning behind the rituals, or the Latin words spoken during the mass. Jean-Marc really didn't care, but Pierre seemed to be searching for meaning in life.

One afternoon on their way home from a soccer game the two friends noticed a dark green building just across the street from the stadium. On the building was a big sign that read *Centre Baptiste*. Out of curiosity they walked inside. It was a quiet reading room, with several young men sitting at tables and reading magazines and newspapers or studying their homework.

Reading room at a Baptist center in Dakar, Senegal

A Senegalese man from the Diola tribe got up from a desk near the door, walked over, and introduced himself. His name was Sékou Diatta and he was the resident director of the Baptist center. Diatta and his wife, who lived in a small apartment behind the center, kept the center clean and protected it from theft. Diatta explained that the center was provided by some people of the Christian religion called Baptists.

Jean-Marc and Pierre were delighted to find the center because they had no place at home to study where it was quiet. Jean-Marc's tiny two-room house was in constant turmoil with Narie yelling at her three young children. The two girls, Rama, age 6, and Seynabou, age 5, were fairly quiet, but the 3-year-old boy, Moussa, was a loud-mouthed terror. It was even worse at Pierre's house. His uncle had 2 wives and 13 children, ranging in age from 4 to 19 years.

Pierre and Jean-Marc began to drop by the Baptist center nearly every afternoon after class. It was on the bus route from their *lycée* to the *quartier* where they lived and less than a kilometer's walk from their homes.

Pierre struck up a close friendship with Diatta, and they often would walk outside into the walled-off courtyard behind the center to talk. An excellent student, Pierre had time to talk and browse through books at the center, while Jean-Marc needed all his time there to study his lessons.

One day Pierre found a book he had never seen before. The title said *Holy Bible.* As he thumbed through the pages, he noticed interesting stories and proverbs. Like most Africans, Pierre was fascinated with proverbs. He took the book over to Diatta and asked him who the author was, pointing out that the title page did not identify the writer.

"Oh," replied Diatta quickly. "That is my Father's book. As my Father inspired them, several people wrote about him and his Son."

"What is your father's name?" asked Pierre.

"My Father's name is Jehovah," replied Diatta, "and he is the God and Creator of the universe. You Muslims call him Allah, but it makes no difference what name you call him. The real difference comes only when you know him per-

Man reading French-language newspaper at a Baptist center in Dakar, Senegal

sonally. Then he becomes your Father, and you become his son.

Intrigued by the conversation, Pierre asked Diatta to tell him more about this god he called Father and why he considered himself a "son of God."

While Jean-Marc sat quietly at the table still studying his lessons, Diatta told Pierre how Jehovah, the creator, had sent his only Son, Jesus, to live in the world as a human being so that through him all people could know and understand God the Father. As Diatta told the story of Jesus, Pierre was fascinated not only with the story itself, but with Diatta's sincerity as he told it. He could tell that Diatta's religion really meant something to him.

Noticing Pierre's intense interest, Diatta suggested that he come to the center on Friday. Farrell Runyan, the Baptist missionary in charge of the center, was to be there and could tell him more about Jesus. Pierre agreed to come.

That afternoon as they walked home, Pierre told Jean-Marc about the *Holy Bible* he had seen. He explained why he wanted to know more about Diatta's God.

As Jean-Marc recalled that afternoon two years ago, he remembered his own lack of interest in what Pierre was saying. He couldn't understand why Pierre was more interested in Diatta's religion than in the girls they usually discussed.

But when Friday came, Pierre talked Jean-Marc into going back to the Baptist center. There they saw with Diatta a barrel-chested white man with wavy gray hair. He appeared to be about 60 years old, although Jean-Marc could never tell the ages of *toubob.*

Diatta called to them, "Meet Pastor Runyan." Jean-Marc noticed how well the missionary spoke French as they exchanged greetings.

After talking for a few moments, Jean-Marc politely excused himself and went over to one of the tables to study. Diatta, Pierre, and Pastor Runyan talked at Diatta's desk for awhile and then went out into the courtyard in the back.

About an hour later, Pierre returned into the reading room and whispered excitedly to Jean-Marc. "You've got to talk to this man. He has told me about Jesus, and I have asked Jesus to live in my heart. Come quickly! Pastor Runyan has to leave in a few minutes."

Although he didn't really want to, Jean-Marc followed his best friend out into the courtyard.

Pierre was so excited he started telling Jean-Marc everything Runyan had been saying. Pierre was convinced that Jesus is the Son of God, that he came into the world as a human being to save people from the sins that separate them from God, that he died on a cross and rose from the dead, and that all who believe in Jesus can through their faith in him have eternal life.

Pointing to a booklet Pastor Runyan had read to him, Pierre said it contained the answer to what he had been

Missionary Farrell E. Runyan and friend in front of a
Baptist center in Dakar, Senegal

searching for in life. When Runyan came to the final page of
the booklet, he had offered to read with Pierre a prayer for
Pierre to accept Jesus as Savior. "I prayed that prayer, Jean-
Marc, and now Jesus lives in my life."

Runyan interrupted at that moment. He understood some
Wolof, which Pierre had lapsed into in his excitement, but he
used French in which he was much more comfortable. He
asked Jean-Marc if he would like to read the booklet and have
the same experience. Out of politeness to the white man and
out of respect for his best friend, Jean-Marc replied yes.

Runyan read each page of the booklet with Jean-Marc, going over each point clearly and simply in French. When they came to the final prayer, Runyan asked Jean-Marc if he would like to pray as Pierre had prayed, and to accept Jesus into his heart and life. Again, out of politeness and respect, Jean-Marc said yes.

When they left the center that day, Pierre had never been happier or more radiant. He repeatedly told Jean-Marc that at last he had found the meaning for which he had been searching but that had eluded him for so long. Jean-Marc was quiet. He had little to say because he really didn't understand why Pierre was so excited. True, he had prayed the prayer too, but he felt little different from the way he had felt when he arrived at the center.

III

Jean-Marc's back was beginning to hurt as he leaned against the coconut palm on the beach. He stood up and walked northward. In the haze ahead, he could barely see the lighthouse atop one of the twin hills jutting out into the Atlantic on Africa's westernmost peninsula. Jagged cliffs separated the beach from the hills where the lighthouse stood. As he continued walking, the outline of a small fishing village loomed in the haze. Jean-Marc saw several fishermen of the Lebu tribe paddling in dugout boats toward shore. Women waited on the beach to clean the morning catch and take it to market for sale that day.

Jean-Marc stopped for a moment. Kicking the sand as he dug his toes into the beach, he turned and headed back down the beach the way he had come. He didn't want to be with people, even the Lebu fishermen. He had so many regrets about the way he had lived his life. Why couldn't he have been more like Pierre?

There had been an immediate change in Pierre's life after he prayed that prayer at the Baptist center on that significant Friday afternoon. At the very moment Pierre's uncle was at Friday afternoon prayers at the Liberté mosque, Pierre was at the Liberté center, asking Christ to come into his life. While Sunni's habitual prayers apparently made no difference in his life, Pierre's prayer that Friday afternoon brought about a radical change in the way he lived.

Pierre began to spend every moment he could at the center,

Fishermen near Dakar, Senegal

talking to Diatta and Pastor Runyan and reading the Bible. His school lessons didn't suffer, although Pierre seemed to whisk through his homework in record speed. Jean-Marc began to see less and less of his best friend that first month after Pierre accepted Christ.

The most radical change came in Pierre's social life. The night after Pierre accepted Christ, Jean-Marc and Pierre had planned to go to the tavern to drink beer with their friends. As a "devout" Muslim, Sunni did not approve of drinking; so, Pierre only drank on Saturday nights when he had permission to stay out late, returning only after his uncle and the rest of the family were in bed. But that first Saturday night after his conversion to Christianity, Pierre refused to go with Jean-Marc to the tavern. Diatta had told him that Christians should not drink, and Pierre wanted to be a "good" Christian.

Jean-Marc went alone to the tavern that night and was glad he did. On his way home, he walked past the home of the Peul girl with the tightly-braided hair and whistled a birdcall. When she heard his secret call, she slipped out of the house and met him in the shadow of a mango tree. Hidden in the shadows, they kissed passionately. But soon a noise from inside the house interrupted them, and the girl slipped from his arms and dashed back into the house for fear of being caught.

When Jean-Marc went to bed, he couldn't sleep and was up early the next morning. He went to Pierre's house to tell him of the previous night, but Pierre wasn't home. He had already gone to the Baptist center for Sunday morning Bible study and worship.

That afternoon Pierre came to see Jean-Marc and shared his painful but hopeful experience of the day. The sermon had been on the sins of the flesh. Pierre regretted his past life so riddled with drinking and "womanizing," as he called it. Yet as guilty as he felt, he had asked God to forgive him; and he knew that through Jesus his past sins had been forgiven. Furthermore, he believed he would have strength to resist such temptations in the future because God would give him the strength.

Jean-Marc had been looking forward to talking to Pierre about the Peul girl, but he never did; he could sense that Pierre would not have approved. It was the first time in their friendship that Jean-Marc had kept anything secret from his best friend.

As the days passed, Jean-Marc could see a definite change

in Pierre's life. He had never seen Pierre so happy. Yet he no longer drank, and he no longer sought the physical joys so important to them both in the past. In contrast, Pierre noticed that Jean-Marc's life had changed not at all.

One month to the day after Pierre had accepted Jesus, the two young men were walking home together. Both were quiet and pensive. Pierre brought up the subject he knew was troubling Jean-Marc.

"What's wrong, Jean-Marc?" he asked. "You act as if I'm not your best friend any more. What's troubling you?"

"I don't know," Jean-Marc replied. "You seem so different, so happy, so full of joy. I don't understand the change that has come over you. I know you say it is because you have become a Christian. But I, too, prayed that prayer four weeks ago today; yet, I don't feel any different."

"You're right. I'm not the same," Pierre replied. "My life had been changed completely. There are peace and joy and meaning to life now that I never experienced or understood before. Now I know that God created me for a purpose, and that purpose is to love him just as he loves me and to share that love with others. Love is the meaning of life, Jean-Marc. Not physical love, but God's love. Love so powerful that it fills my life from the depths of my soul, where God himself now dwells.

"Jean-Marc, let me ask you something," Pierre continued. "One month ago today, when you asked Jesus to come into your life, did you feel the power of this love surge in your heart?"

Jean-Marc was silent for a moment, kicking a rock in the pathway and sending it skipping through the sand. "No, not really. I don't guess I really felt anything."

"Then why did you pray the prayer if it didn't mean anything to you?"

"I guess because you wanted me to so much," Jean-Marc replied.

"Then that's the problem," Pierre concluded. "You didn't really ask Jesus into your heart because you wanted to experience his love and forgiveness. You did it because you wanted to please me. Let me ask you something else. You've seen how happy I have been since I accepted Jesus as Savior. Do you want to experience this same joy and love?"

"Oh, yes," replied Jean-Marc with sincerity. "But I don't know how. I've forgotten what the prayer says, and we don't have a copy of the booklet."

"We don't need one," Pierre said. "Let's stop right here, and I'll help you say the prayer that will change your life just the way it changed mine."

Right in the middle of *Avenue de la Liberté* Jean-Marc and Pierre sat down on a bench under the shade of a small mango tree. On each side of the island in the center of the divided boulevard, honking and roaring loudly, taxis and buses whizzed by the two young men seated alone on the bench. There on the streets of Dakar, Jean-Marc confessed his sins in the presence of his best friend, asking God to forgive him and to fill his soul with love and joy and peace. When they arose, tears of joy streamed down both black faces, glistening in the afternoon sun. From that moment on, they were blood brothers in a new and different way.

IV

Lost in the vivid memories of the experience that occurred two years before, Jean-Marc had almost walked past the park where he started his stroll up the beach. Suddenly he knew where he would go, what he would do.

Quickly he walked to the boulevard and waited for the bus. He might not know the answers to the questions that were haunting him, but he knew where to go for help. For the first time that day, he was in a hurry.

As the bus traveled down *Avenue de la Liberté*, he looked out the window and prayed with thanksgiving when he passed the small mango tree where he and Pierre had prayed together two years ago.

Two kilometers farther, he got off the bus just across from the soccer stadium and crossed the street. Four houses from the corner stood the dark green building with bright yellow letters over the semicircular arches framing the doors. The sign said *Centre Baptiste.*

It was still early, but the doors were locked. Jean-Marc went around to the back and knocked. As he had hoped, Diatta was still there, cleaning up the center.

Pierre's death had been almost as traumatic for Diatta as it had been for Jean-Marc. Diatta and Pierre had become very close friends; yet for some strange reason, Jean-Marc and Diatta had never become close friends. Jean-Marc had never been as active in the Baptist center as his best friend. He would never admit it, but deep down Jean-Marc still felt that Diatta had come between him and Pierre. Lacking Pierre's spiritual maturity, Jean-Marc had not wanted to talk to Diatta with any real depth about his feelings, even after Pierre's death.

At that moment, Jean-Marc realized that he had allowed petty jealousy to deprive him of the comfort and understanding of a concerned fellow Christian. He deeply regretted his past feelings toward Diatta.

When Diatta came to the door, Jean-Marc said he urgently needed to talk to him. From the look on his face, Diatta could tell Jean-Marc was deeply troubled and had spent a sleepless night. He suggested they go out into the courtyard to talk.

There Jean-Marc told Diatta about the terrible nightmares he had been experiencing since Pierre's death. He shared his doubts and his gnawing questions: If God was calling Pierre to be a pastor, why would God allow him to be killed in such a tragic accident before he had been able to fulfill that calling? Why did Pierre die instead of himself? Why was he having these nightmares? What did they mean?

Diatta had no more answers to the haunting questions than Jean-Marc, but he did offer a suggestion. "Why don't you come back today at four o'clock, when Pastor Runyan will be here? He knows the Bible far better than I do. Maybe he can help you find answers to the questions that are plaguing you."

With that glimmer of hope, Jean-Marc left for the market to buy some fish and rice with what was left of the few coins in his pocket. He couldn't go home because he didn't want his father or Narie to know he had skipped classes today. He would just have to kill time until four o'clock in the afternoon.

THE CENTER OF HIS WILL

I

 Jean-Marc had not eaten all day. He reached into his pocket and pulled out all the money he had. It was less than 200 francs, not enough to still hunger pangs and cover his bus fare to school for the rest of the week. Suddenly he had an idea.

He would go to the Colabane market near where Alphonse, one of his friends from the *lycée*, worked in his father's shop. Alphonse, who was having trouble with his grades anyway, had dropped out of school several months before because his father was ill. By now Alphonse was bored with his work. Selling flour and millet from big sacks that his father bought from a wholesaler was no longer more fun than school. He was always delighted when Jean-Marc or one of his other friends from the *lycée* stopped by to visit.

Once before when Jean-Marc had gone by the market to see Alphonse, he had worked in the shop for an hour or two while Alphonse slipped off to see Dorothé, his girl friend. Dorothé worked at home, keeping her small brothers and sisters and washing clothes for her mother.

Jean-Marc took the bus to the market, thankful that by now the crowds had thinned out. It was almost noon, and most of the people at the market were going home to eat and to take their afternoon *sieste* (nap). Alphonse usually took his

Pedestrian in Dakar, Senegal, passing by a market stall

sieste in a hammock in his shop, sleeping lightly for fear that someone would try to steal his father's goods. Some people closed for the afternoon, but Alphonse's father refused to. He or Alphonse always slept lightly in the hammock in order to be there if someone came to buy some flour.

The market area was more crowded than Jean-Marc expected. The broad walkway was thick with people, and the cloth merchants were still doing a brisk business, selling yards of material from bolts of brightly colored cloth stacked haphazardly on rows and rows of tables in the open air.

Walking past the open-air cloth market, Jean-Marc turned to the right and went down a row of stalls where the day's fish catch was being sold. The smell was overpowering. There was no refrigeration in the market, and some of the fish were already beginning to spoil in the 100-degree heat. Flies swarmed everywhere, but the fish vendors simply brushed them away with light brooms in a never-ending chore. One of the stalls was selling fresh goat meat from a young kid slaughtered that morning. Past the fish and meat stalls, Jean-Marc jostled his way through a group of women buying fresh vegetables and fruits. There were cabbages, tomatoes, sweet potatoes, squash, pineapples, bananas, avocados, oranges, and mangoes piled in neat stacks everywhere. Finally Jean-Marc reached Alphonse's shop.

Alphonse was glad to see Jean-Marc. They exchanged polite greetings, going through the ritual according to Senegalese custom, not because they really cared but simply out of habit. Alphonse had already been lying in his hammock, reading a cheap paperback he had bought in a market stall.

Jean-Marc asked Alphonse how he and Dorothé were getting along, and Alphonse stared off into space with a dreamy, faraway gaze.

"That girl is wonderful," Alphonse responded. "She gets more beautiful every day."

Alphonse didn't say more, but Jean-Marc knew what he was thinking. Jean-Marc was careful with his next words. "I wonder what she's doing right now?" he asked.

"She's probably just finishing feeding the children and is getting them ready to take their naps," Alphonse said. Then, just as if it were his own idea, his face lit up with excitement and Alphonse suggested to Jean-Marc, "My friend, do you think you could watch the shop for me for an hour or two while I slip away to see Dorothé?"

"Well, I don't know," Jean-Marc replied. "I was on my way home to get something to eat. I haven't eaten all day, and I'm starved. I don't think I could last until you get back without eating something."

"Why don't you buy some rice and goat stew in the market?" asked Alphonse.

"I just don't have enough money. I've already spent most of my bus fare for the week, and if I bought some stew here at the market, I wouldn't have enough for my bus fare home."

Alphonse pondered the situation and came up with the suggestion Jean-Marc was hoping he would propose. "I'll tell you what. If you will watch the shop for me, I'll buy you some

Open-air cloth market at Dakar, Senegal

goat stew and rice. It's worth that much for me to be able to get away from this place for awhile to see Dorothé."

With Alphonse's 50 francs in his pocket, Jean-Marc walked over to the cook stall area in the market and bought a bowl of goat stew and rice. A Wolof woman was selling the food from an open stall where four big caldrons were bubbling and boiling, each sitting on three rocks with a wood fire underneath. One kettle contained rice, one was full of goat stew, a third was a fish stew, and the fourth was a cassava porridge. The Wolof woman, perspiring profusely because of the heat of the fires, constantly stirred the four caldrons with a long wooden paddle. Every day she cooked the four pots of food in the market, selling all she could to the people who came there to shop. It was the Senegalese version of a fast-food place.

When Jean-Marc returned to the shop with his bowl of rice and goat stew, Alphonse left to visit Dorothé. Jean-Marc chuckled to himself at how cleverly he had succeeded in getting Alphonse to do exactly what he wanted him to do. The beauty of the whole thing was that Jean-Marc got a free meal, a hammock where he could take his *sieste,* and something to occupy his time until his appointment with Pastor Runyan. Alphonse had promised to return in time to open for business at about three o'clock, after *sieste* time.

II

Alphonse was late getting back, as Jean-Marc suspected he would be; and they talked until after four o'clock, primarily about Alphonse's afternoon with Dorothé. Jean-Marc knew he would be late for his appointment with Pastor Runyan, but he wasn't worried. Time matters little in West Africa, and Jean-Marc had vowed long before never to be a slave to the clock like the *toubob.*

It was 4:45 before Jean-Marc arrived by bus at the Baptist center. He hoped Pastor Runyan had not left yet, but if he had, there was always tomorrow.

When Jean-Marc walked into the center, Diatta was upset. He scolded him for being so late, telling Jean-Marc he was thoughtless. Fortunately, however, Runyan was still at the center.

The men talked for awhile at Diatta's table, exchanging pleasantries but avoiding the principal subject that all three knew would come up later. Finally, impatient to finish and go home, Runyan abruptly got to the point. "Diatta tells me you wanted to talk to me about a problem," Runyan said in French. "Would you like to go out and sit under the tree where it's cooler?"

Although he was offended by Runyan's brusqueness, Jean-Marc never hinted his feelings. "That would be nice," he replied politely.

Actually, Jean-Marc didn't think that was a good idea at all because he preferred to stay at Diatta's desk. If they went to the back courtyard to sit under the tree, Diatta would have to stay inside. Somehow, Jean-Marc felt uneasy talking alone with Pastor Runyan. Runyan was a very friendly man, always happy and joking, but something about him made Jean-Marc feel uncomfortable. He didn't know what it was, perhaps just his abrupt, straight-to-the-point American way of dealing with people. Jean-Marc was more at ease with the subtle, roundabout African way. But Runyan was the *pasteur*, and Jean-Marc was reluctant to say he did not want to go to the back courtyard to talk alone with him. Then he had an idea.

"There's a cool breeze from the north," Jean-Marc observed. "It might be better to sit in the portico and lean against the arches where we can feel the cool wind. The breeze can't reach the back courtyard very easily. That way, maybe Diatta can join us."

Runyan agreed it was a good idea but told Diatta he would need to look inside from time to time to make sure no one tried to steal any of the books or magazines in the reading room. They would have more privacy in the portico than at Diatta's desk, he agreed.

Outside, Runyan once again came straight to the point. "Diatta tells me you've been having nightmares," he began. "Tell me about them."

Wary at first, Jean-Marc cautiously recounted his haunting and recurring dream and his feelings about Pierre's death. At several points Diatta interrupted, adding details that Jean-Marc had skimmed over superficially. Diatta's obvious respect for Runyan and his complete openness and trust in the missionary helped Jean-Marc to open up and speak more freely.

Runyan was obviously surprised when he learned that Pierre had felt that God was calling him to be a pastor and a missionary to his own people. He quickly turned to Diatta and remarked:

"Why didn't you tell me Pierre wanted to be a pastor? I didn't know until now!"

Diatta replied that Pierre had told him in complete confidence. He also explained Pierre's fear that Sunni might find out and force him to return to Timbuktu before he finished his education. Pierre was afraid that if he told anyone at the center other than Diatta, who was sworn to secrecy, the word might get back to his uncle. "I just couldn't tell you about it until Pierre told me it was all right to do so," Diatta explained.

Coming to Diatta's defense, Jean-Marc added that both he and Pierre had been worried after Jean-Marc told Zukono that Pierre had accepted Christ, explaining why they were afraid Zukono would tell Sunni. Then Jean-Marc went on to tell Pastor Runyan about his heated argument with Zukono the night before.

Jean-Marc did not go into detail about his "blood brother" relationship with Pierre or his father's argument that he did not fulfill his reponsibilities as "best friend" after Pierre's death. Jean-Marc didn't think the missionary would understand his father's superstitious beliefs and customs. But he did tell Pastor Runyan his father's claim that Pierre's spirit was coming back from the grave to haunt him and to cause the horrible nightmares.

"*Pasteur,* what do you think is causing these nightmares?" asked Jean-Marc.

Runyan was silent for awhile, and then he replied:"I don't know, but I suspect it may be because you feel guilty that Pierre was the one who died in the accident instead of you. Let me ask you something. Have you felt guilty because Pierre pushed you out of the way and died instead of you?"

Jean-Marc hung his head in contrition and admitted that he did feel guilty. Then he expressed his true feelings.

"You may be right. I have been burdened with guilt because Pierre was the one who died instead of me. What I can't understand is why God would allow this to happen! Pierre was the one, not I, who had felt God was calling him to be a pastor. Why would God allow someone he was calling to the ministry to die in such a tragic accident before he had been able to fulfill his calling? Why was Pierre the one to die? Why was I the one to live?"

"I cannot say," Runyan replied. "Perhaps God had a purpose that we don't know or understand. Perhaps God was trying to teach you something through Pierre's death. We don't always understand God's permissive will, but we must always seek to understand how God can take something that seems tragic to us at the time and work good from it.

"Pierre was seeking to find the center of God's will for his life. He had placed his absolute trust in God. Maybe that's all God required from him. We just don't know and we will never know until we, too, stand before God's presence in heaven and all things are made clear to us. What we must do is seek God's will daily and ask how he can use each experience in life to teach us to seek the center of his will, just as Pierre did."

"But how can you know God's will?" Jean-Marc asked. "Pierre seemed so sure God was calling him to be a pastor and to take the gospel to his own people, but I could never understand how he knew that this was God's will. He couldn't explain it. He said he just knew. But I don't know what God's will is for my life. How can I know for sure?"

III

Runyan paused for a moment. This was a question he had struggled with all his life. Then he looked at Jean-Marc earnestly. "You just have to trust God completely every day and seek his guidance and direction every day," Runyan replied. "There may be weeks and months when you won't know; but at some time God always reveals his will to those who seek it. You have to pray each day; you have to read and study his word each day; you have to maintain fellowship with other Christians who are seeking his will. Often it is through others that God reveals his will. Often it is through his church. Sometimes God reveals his will in daily circumstances by closing one door and opening another.

"Let me ask you something very personal," Runyan added quietly. "Have you deep in your heart wondered if the reason God allowed Pierre to die and you to live is because God wants *you* to be a pastor and to fulfill the same calling Pierre had felt?"

Like a razor-sharp dagger, Pastor Runyan's words pierced

Jean-Marc's heart. His eyes widened with fear, and his hands trembled with fright. His throat and mouth dried as if filled with sand from the Sahara. For several moments he couldn't speak.

"I don't know," he stammered in a hoarse voice. Putting his hand to his head, rubbing his temples with his thumb and forefinger, Jean-Marc repeated again, "I just don't know."

In the silence that followed, Jean-Marc knew what he answered was a lie. He *did* know. The thought had crossed his mind several times, but he had refused to admit it even to himself. He didn't want to think about that possibility. He didn't even want to acknowledge that the thought had entered his mind.

Looking into Pastor Runyan's clear blue eyes, Jean-Marc confided: "I don't know what God's will is for my life, but I want to know. I just don't know how to find God's will. What should I do?"

"It will take time for you to grow spiritually and to understand God's plan for your life," Runyan replied, "but I will try to help you. Let me make several suggestions. First of all, I think you need to practice a daily, disciplined quiet time when you can read the Bible and pray privately. As you pray, let God speak to you in the silence of your aloneness with him. He probably won't speak in an audible voice, but you may be able to hear him in the stillness and depths of your soul. Secondly, I think you need to study the Bible with more depth than simply reading it like any other book. It might be good for you to enroll in the Baptist Correspondence Course that my wife, Libby, handles for the Baptist Mission. If you're interested, you can talk to her after the sewing class here at the center on Tuesday afternoon. These courses are called *A la Découverte de la Bible.* I think they will help you discover and understand the Bible.

"There's a third thing I think you need to do," Runyan continued. "I've noticed that although Pierre was very faithful and active in attending the worship service each Sunday here at the center, you haven't come very often in the past. I think that regular worship with others who are seeking God's will would help you as you struggle to find God's will. One thing you will discover quickly is that you are not alone in your quest and that there is strength in sharing with others. As you grow in your understanding, you may want to teach a Bible study class or accept some other leadership responsibility at either this center, or one of the two other centers Baptists operate in the Dakar area.

"Now, I've been very frank and direct," Runyan concluded. "How do you feel about what we've discussed?"

Jean-Marc was silent for several moments because he couldn't put his feelings into words easily. He felt better, but he still felt uncomfortable—a little frightened and scared. Finally he said, "You've helped me come to grips with the real question that I have not even wanted to admit before—that God might be calling me to be a pastor to carry out that task Pierre was not able to fulfill. That's scary—and my guilt has been so overpowering that this may be the reason for my nightmares. I appreciate your practical suggestions on how I can know and follow God's will. More than anything else, that's what I want to do."

By the time Pastor Runyan and Jean-Marc had finished their conversation, it was time to close the center for the night. As the last students left the reading room and Diatta locked the doors, Runyan and Jean-Marc stayed inside. Runyan turned to Jean-Marc and asked quietly, "Would you like to pray with me and Diatta—that God will cleanse your soul of this terrible guilt you feel and help you find the center of God's will for your life?"

When Jean-Marc nodded his agreement, he, Diatta, and Runyan walked to a private corner in the back of the room, where they knelt and prayed. A feeling of relief flooded Jean-Marc's heart. For the first time in weeks, he seemed to be able really to pray. The words gushed out in torrents, as if they had been pent up inside for months. As never before, he felt the presence of God. He rejoiced and thanked God that Pastor Runyan had told him what he needed to hear. Silent tears of concern streamed down his cheeks.

After they had prayed together, both Diatta and Runyan

embraced Jean-Marc and assured him of their continued prayers and concern. Both urged him to come to the center any time he needed to talk or to pray.

After Runyan left, Jean-Marc lingered awhile and chatted with Diatta. Not until he was at the bus stop did he realize how exhausted he was. It had been a long, traumatic day, but for the first time in two months, he knew he would sleep well. He faced the future with new hope.

DESIRE FOR KNOWLEDGE

I

A tense excitement that ranged somewhere between nervous fear and effervescent anticipation overwhelmed Jean-Marc when he opened the door of the white, French-made car and greeted the missionary couple in the front seat.

Behind the wheel was a swarthy, thin-faced American with black hair and dark glasses. Seated beside him was a short, pleasantly plump woman with hair the color of her husband's deeply tanned skin.

Paul and Peggy Grossman warmly welcomed Jean-Marc and told him how glad they were he was able to teach the Bible lesson that Sunday morning at the Gran Yoff preaching point. Comé Théophile, who usually taught the lesson at Gran Yoff, was sick. "Of course, I could have taught the lesson, but I always think it is better if an African can be the teacher," Grossman said, as he steered the car around a dusty curve. "Sometimes the young people ask questions that can be answered best in Wolof rather than French, and we are always more comfortable when someone who speaks both French and Wolof can teach the lesson," Grossman added.

Jean-Marc didn't say so, but the butterflies in his stomach seemed to be beating rigid wings against his internal organs. He had never taught the Bible lesson before at Gran Yoff or at any of the three Baptist centers in the Dakar area.

It had been six months since Pastor Runyan had advised him to start teaching a Bible class, and this was his first opportunity. A lot had happened since that time that he had prayed with Pastor Runyan. As a result of that spiritual experience, Jean-Marc had not experienced another of his nightmares. They had simply stopped. And with the end of the nightmares came a new spiritual dedication and a new quest for knowledge of the Bible and spiritual growth. But Jean-Marc realized he was still "a babe in Jesus." The responsibility of teaching the Bible class seemed overwhelming.

As they rode along, Jean-Marc asked Grossman what to expect that Sunday. "I've never been to Gran Yoff before," Jean-Marc said. "Tell me what it's going to be like."

"Well, of course, our preaching point is located in one of the poorest sections of Dakar. Most of the people there have had little formal education. We have services in a little building on one of the major streets of Gran Yoff. Occasionally I preach or show a film, but mostly we just have a song service and a Bible study."

"How many people do you expect?" Jean-Marc asked anxiously.

"We never know," replied Grossman. "Sometimes there are only two or three. Sometimes the room will be jammed with 10 or 15. Response here is slow, even perhaps slower than in the rest of Dakar. And that's *really* slow. I admit I get discouraged because the response is so slow. In 12 years of organized Baptist work here in Dakar, there are fewer than a dozen baptized believers. Of course, there are more than a hundred who regularly attend the services at our three centers and the preaching points, and almost a hundred others who attend the English-language worship service at the American Embassy. But the response has been terribly discouraging when you figure we've averaged only one baptized believer a year in this 90-percent Muslim country."

Pastor Grossman's frustration with the lack of response actually was a little encouraging to Jean-Marc. He was hoping there would be only a few who showed up at Gran Yoff this morning, for he wasn't sure he was ready yet to teach the Bible lesson. If only a few were present, maybe he wouldn't be so nervous. He had a strange feeling of ambivalence about teaching the lesson. The night before as he prepared, he had all the confidence in the world that he could do a good job. But this morning, with butterflies in his stomach, he wasn't so sure.

Before he realized it, they had turned up a wide, sandy road and stopped just beyond the small building where the Bible study was to be held. While the Grossmans greeted the neighbors next door, Jean-Marc unloaded the car. Then he joined the missionary couple. Cheerfully they paid their respects to the family living next to the center and joked with several young women who were walking down the street. Children began to gather, and Grossman teased one youngster, asking where he had been for the last three weeks. Three young men from the neighborhood arrived, and the Grossmans went inside the small building with them. Jean-Marc followed. It was time to start.

On a nail in the wall, Grossman hung a portfolio of large song sheets with the words to hymns written in large print on each sheet. Peggy took a big accordion from a black carrying case. She strapped it around her shoulders and turned toward one of the young men dressed in a blue shirt and grey pants as Grossman handed him a small set of bongo drums. He explained to the three young men that normally Théophile would play the guitar and teach, but because he was sick today, Jean-Marc would teach the lesson. Then they began to sing.

For almost 30 minutes the Grossmans, Jean-Marc, and the three young men sang hymns to the frenzied beat of the drums and the melody of the accordion. At the door, dozens

of children crowded to listen, but no one else came inside.
Finally, assuming no one else was coming, Grossman introduced Jean-Marc again and asked him to lead the Bible
study.

Before Jean-Marc started, Grossman shooed away the
children, warning them that they had to leave now that the
singing was over. He explained to Jean-Marc that he hated to
make the children leave, but they wouldn't understand the
lesson and they made so much noise and created such a dis-
turbance that the three young men couldn't get anything out
of the lesson if he allowed the children to stay.

Jean-Marc began the lesson. It was on John 14:1-31, the
words Jesus spoke during the Passover meal to his disciples
concerning his resurrection and the coming of the Holy
Spirit. Jean-Marc believed the passage was especially appropriate for a Muslim society, for in it Jesus told his
disciples, "I am the way, the truth, and the life: no man
cometh unto the Father, but by me."

Despite his intense preparation, the lesson went badly for
Jean-Marc. He forgot everything he had planned to say. His
mouth became dry as a Sahel water hole just before rainy
season, and he stuttered and stammered as if his mouth were
filled with mud. When he tried to write on the chalkboard,
even his writing was shaky. He rambled from point to point,
verse to verse, often skipping back to an earlier verse to cover
something he had forgotten to say. He tried to get the three
young men to ask questions, but they sat as silently and
stoically as statues. The one in the blue shirt who had played
the drums so enthusiastically yawned and obviously fought
to stay awake. At several points, Grossman interrupted to
make a point, and each time he did, it made Jean-Marc feel
worse. He had already thought of the same idea and had
jotted it down the night before on his notes, but he could not
say the words clearly that morning.

The lesson was supposed to last about 30 minutes, with
time for questions at the end, but after 10 minutes, Jean-
Marc had said all he knew to say. He asked if the young men
had any questions. There was silence. Only the sounds of the

children playing in the street filled the room. Jean-Marc turned to the missionary couple and asked, "Pastor Grossman, do you have anything to add?"

With just a few brief sentences, Grossman summed up the lesson and posed several questions that he felt the passage raised. He turned to the young man in the blue shirt and asked him pointedly: "Isaka, what do you believe Jesus meant when he said, 'I am the way, the truth, and the life, and no man cometh unto the Father, but by me'?"

The question started an intense debate among the three young men present. One of the three, Denis, argued that believing in Jesus was the only way to know God. But the two others disagreed. Isaka was extremely vocal, saying that Jesus was only one of *many* ways to know God—that one could also know God through following the teachings of Mohammed or through nature or through many other religions.

Grossman summarized the teachings of Jesus and the Christian belief that God sent his son, Jesus, to show humankind the way to salvation. After a closing hymn and a prayer, the service was over.

As they drove away, Jean-Marc was silent. He felt he had done poorly with his first opportunity to teach Bible study. Only when Pastor Grossman took over did the young men begin to respond.

II

Two weeks later at the *Centre Baptiste,* Jean-Marc sat at one of the tables in the reading room and finished the final questions on what he felt was the best book yet in the Baptist Correspondence Course. It was entitled *Le Merveilleux Plan de Dieu* (The Marvelous Plan of God), and it had helped Jean-Marc more than anything else he had ever read. He thought he had done well on the final assignment and could hardly wait to get his grade.

In the six months since Runyan had made the suggestion,

Jean-Marc had completed four of the five books in the first part of the Baptist Correspondence Course. He had studied books entitled *Qui Est Jesus?* (Who Is Jesus?) and two books on the Gospel according to St. Mark. He had only one book more, *Principes Fondamentaux de l'Enseignement Biblique* (Fundamental Principles of Biblical Teaching), before he earned his diploma from the basic level courses and could qualify for the four courses in the advanced study.

Jean-Marc was glad to be able to finish the last lesson that afternoon. He was invited to have dinner that night at the home of Frank and Sally Cawthon, and he looked forward to handing her his final papers. She was in charge of the Baptist Correspondence Course while the Runyans were in the United States on furlough.

Jean-Marc enjoyed being with the Cawthons. They were quite young, and Jean-Marc was impressed that Cawthon was the business manager for the Baptist mission. Yet, even though he did not call himself a pastor and she was a home-maker, Jean-Marc knew that both Cawthon and his wife were very active at the center.

Frank Cawthon had arranged in advance to meet Jean-Marc at the Baptist center at 5:15 p.m. that day. The Cawthons and the Runyans lived in a mission compound not far from the lighthouse and it was difficult to get there by bus. Cawthon was to pick up Jean-Marc after completing some business at the government office, where he was trying to get a building permit for the construction of new mission property.

Promptly at 5:15, Cawthon arrived at the center, and Jean-Marc got into the front seat beside him. Obviously, the American was frustrated. For the fifth time, he had waited for three hours in the government office, only to be told that the permit was not ready.

When they arrived at the mission compound, Jean-Marc jumped out of the car and opened the wide gate to allow Cawthon to drive into the walled-off area. On each side of the wide driveway and spacious lawns towered stuccoed two-story houses. Jean-Marc knew that the lower floor of the building on the left was devoted to offices for the Baptist mission and that Pastor Farrell and his wife lived in the apartment above the offices. The building on the right included a guest house for visitors and the two-story home of the Cawthons.

Jean-Marc was somewhat apprehensive because he had never visited in the home of an American before, much less eaten with an American family. As they walked together toward the Cawthons' home, two young children came running out to meet them. The missionary introduced his two children, Jayne and Matthew. Then they all went inside.

Jean-Marc knew better than to show his feelings, but he was amazed at the size of the house as compared with the small dwelling in which he lived. It was neatly and tastefully furnished with comfortable, padded chairs and a long couch. Jean-Marc saw household equipment he had never seen before in somebody's house: a refrigerator, a gas range, an automatic dishwasher, flush toilets downstairs and upstairs, a washing machine and dryer, and even a hot water heater. Deep down, he envied the American missionaries. They had everything that he had ever dreamed of possessing. He knew from Diatta that missionaries also received a salary. But Diatta had reminded him that these "luxuries" enabled them to live somewhat as they were accustomed to live, and at the same time to devote their major energies to proclaiming the gospel to the people of Dakar.

Despite all their wonderful possessions, the Cawthons seemed to accept Jean-Marc just as if he were one of their family. They made him feel at ease by their mannerisms and by the informal way they related to him and to each other.

Jean-Marc immediately liked the two children. Although Matthew was a little shy, Jayne became his friend at once. It wasn't long before she was sitting on his lap, talking to him in French. Although Jean-Marc knew that the Cawthons spoke English at home and that Matthew and Jayne addressed their parents in English, which he did not understand, Jayne spoke French amazingly well for a beginner. In some respects, her French was even better than her father's and mother's.

During the meal Jean-Marc once again was apprehensive. He was unfamiliar with American manners for eating. After the blessing, the missionary passed the salad bowl to his wife. She filled a small bowl to the left of her plate with salad and then poured an oily liquid over the fresh, crisp lettuce. Jean-Marc followed her example. When he took his first bite, he almost gagged because of the bitter-tasting oil all over the fresh lettuce. He couldn't understand why *toubob* ruined good vegetables with a sauce they called salad dressing. He would have to force himself to eat every bite so he would not offend his hosts.

As they chatted in French, Cawthon asked Jean-Marc if he had ever eaten pizza.

"No," replied Jean-Marc. "What is pizza?"

"Well, you will find out in a moment," Cawthon replied. "It is an Italian pastry with a heavy layer of cheese and tomato sauce on top. Even though it is Italian in origin, it is truly an American food. We hope you like it."

Frank Cawthon sliced the pizza and passed it to Jean-Marc and each member of the family, serving himself last. Jean-Marc noticed that Sally Cawthon cut her pizza with a knife and ate it with a fork; but Cawthon picked up his pizza with his fingers and took a big bite from the pie-shaped slice. Jean-Marc didn't know what to do. He had understood most Americans felt it was impolite to eat with your fingers. But maybe it was customary in American culture for the men to eat one way and the women to eat another. He decided to follow Cawthon's example.

His first bite of pizza perplexed Jean-Marc. He couldn't decide if he liked it or not. Finally, he decided it was edible, although not nearly so tasty as fish or goat stew served with rice. It was mild by comparison to the hot sauce that was served with fish stew. After several more bites, he decided he liked pizza. It was a little bland but quite tasty.

After the meal, Sally Cawthon left the dirty dishes on the table, and they all went into the living room to talk. Jean-Marc decided now was the time to present her with the completed work on the final lesson in his correspondence course.

Her eyes lit up with amazement when he handed her the papers.

"Why, Jean-Marc," she exclaimed, "I can't believe you've finished the last lesson so quickly! In less than six months, you've completed four courses. No one has ever completed the correspondence work so quickly as you. I just hope that in your haste to finish, you have done your work well."

"I've tried," replied Jean-Marc. "This was the most exciting and interesting course of all, and I've learned more from it than any other. I've gone as fast as I could, for I've been especially anxious to complete this past course on *The Marvelous Plan of God.*"

"Sally and I have been talking about you," interjected Cawthon. "We both have been amazed at how fast you've completed your work. But both of us feel that you could do better work if you would take a little more time and study a little harder," he added. "There is no reason to rush through the courses as fast as you have done, especially if taking a little more time would enable you to learn more and achieve higher grades."

Jean-Marc looked down at his sandals, realizing that he had made a mistake by rushing through the study so quickly. They were right. His grades were not as good as they should be, although they were far better than his grades at the *lycée* lately. On the first course, "Who Is Jesus," Jean-Marc had made a B, and on the two courses on the Gospel of Mark, he had made a C on each. He felt sure he would at least make a B on this course, and maybe even an A.

Cawthon paused for a moment and then added: "One reason we'd like to see you take more time and improve your grades is because Sally and I both feel you have tremendous potential. We'd like to see you not only complete the correspondence courses, but also enroll in the Theological Education by Extension courses that Pastor Grossman is planning to start in September. There are three other young men who are hoping to enroll, and Sally and I both feel that you would learn a great deal from these courses. But they are much more difficult than the correspondence courses, and if your grades are not good on the correspondence courses, it won't appear that you are qualified to take the TEE courses. Think about it, and let us know if you are interested in enrolling in the TEE courses. I'll be glad to speak to Pastor Grossman about it."

Jean-Marc said he was definitely interested in studying Theological Education by Extension and would like very much to enroll in the first classes in Dakar. He told the Cawthons that he felt sure his grades on the course he had just completed would be better than his work on the previous correspondence courses.

But two weeks later, when Sally Cawthon had finished grading his lessons, the grade was disappointing. It was another C on the course he felt had been his best work.

III

The morning after his visit with the Cawthons, even before the first cockcrow, Jean-Marc awoke with a start. This time there was no moaning, no screaming.

It was not another nightmare that awakened him, but a dream or vision that was almost as clear as if it had actually happened. The memory of the dream lingered long after he awoke.

In his dream, he saw an African walking down the streets of a mud-brick village with flat roofs. Muslim women with veils over their faces and men wearing turbans and fezzes jostled down the narrow, dusty streets.

The African would stop and talk to the villagers. Whenever he met people who were sick or infirm, the man in Jean-Marc's dream would touch them and they would be healed. As he walked down the streets, crowds of people began to follow him. When they came to a mosque, the man walked inside the courtyard and began to preach to the crowds.

But this was no marabout, no holy Muslim priest. There was a compassion in the man's voice, a concern that Jean-Marc could detect was deeper than he had ever heard before.

But Jean-Marc could not recognize who the man was. His

face was an out-of-focus blur. All he could see was the man's eyes, which pierced deep into his heart.

Finally, the face began to take shape in Jean-Marc's mind. At first he thought the man was Pierre. Then the face changed, and it looked like classical paintings he had seen of Jesus. But the image of the face changed again, and Jean-Marc suddenly realized that it was his own face he saw.

When he got up at 4:00 A.M., unable to sleep after his dream, Jean-Marc walked outside to sit alone beneath the huge baobab tree in the courtyard where less than a year earlier he had argued with his father so fiercely.

As he thought about the dream, he wondered what it meant. Where was this strange village with the flat roofs? He knew it did not look like a village in Senegal. Then it dawned on him. He remembered the photograph Pierre had once shown him of his hometown in Timbuktu, 900 miles away on the edge of the Sahara, in the center of Mali. The buildings in Pierre's photo of Timbuktu had the same flat roofs and the same mud-brick constructions.

What did the dream mean? With a sense of excitement, Jean-Marc thought he already knew, but he wasn't sure. He believed it was God's way of calling him to be a missionary to the Songhai people in Timbuktu, to carry out the challenge Pierre had given him as he lay dying.

There in the silence of the night, beneath the baobab tree, Jean-Marc prayed humbly and simply: "Lord, if that's what you want me to do and if that's where you want me to go, I will go wherever you lead and do whatever you reveal to me is your will. Help me to know your will and to do it."

Jean-Marc walked back into the front room of his father's house and lay down on his sleeping mat. He was too excited to sleep, but he decided to try to rest. He did not want to awaken Zukono or the rest of the family. He knew it would be better not to mention anything to his father about his dream. Zukono would not understand or approve of Jean-Marc's even considering the possibility of being a missionary to the Songhai people of Timbuktu.

But he had to talk to someone. He wished Pastor Runyan

were back from his furlough, for it was he who had helped him interpret the meaning of his nightmares.

Later in the day he would share his dream and vision with Diatta, and maybe Diatta would reaffirm his interpretation of the meaning of the vision. Maybe he would also talk to Frank Cawthon about it.

As peace flooded his soul, Jean-Marc relaxed on his sleeping mat. Despite his excitement, rest came. And soon he was asleep again, content in his dreams for the future.

EDUCATIONAL CONFRONTATION

I

The rain pelted Jean-Marc's face like thousands of prickly pellets as he ran down the street toward the bus stop. He still had a half-dozen blocks to go, and already his shirt was soaked. As he ran barefoot down the street with his sandals stuffed beneath his shirt, his left foot hit a hidden pothole, splashing muddy water all over his clean trousers. Almost losing his balance, he struggled not to fall.

As he regained his gait, two words began to alternate in his mind with each stride he took.

Étudier . . . s'appliquer . . . étudier . . . s'appliquer.

With each splash of his feet in the water-filled street, the words pounded his mind with a steady rhythm, building with intensity when his feet hit the pavement.

Left foot, right foot, left, right. It was as if his feet were hands beating an African drum, and his head were the drum reverberating with the two words!

"Study . . . try hard . . . study . . . try hard."

Winded and exhausted, not only from the physical strain of running in the rain but also from the mental anguish of perhaps the toughest day of his life, Jean-Marc finally slowed his pace to a breathless jog and then to a walk. There was no use running. He was still two blocks from the bus stop, and he was already so soaked that running would not keep him any drier.

It was mid-June, and the annual rainy season had started in Dakar. In Senegal there are only two seasons—dry season and rainy season. It is hot the year around, the only cool time being when the harmattan winds blow the dust of the Sahara into Senegal each December. Then it is cool only at nights.

A year had passed since Jean-Marc's vivid dream had prompted him to respond to what he felt was God's call to be a missionary to the people of Timbuktu.

Everyone with whom he shared his sense of calling urged him to prepare himself with intense Bible study. He had taken Frank Cawthon's advice and enrolled in the course taught by Pastor Grossman as part of the new Theological Education by Extension.

It had been the busiest year of Jean-Marc's entire life, the year of most intense study. And this day, June 17, had been the most intense and exhausting day of the year.

Jean-Marc had crammed most of the night before, finally falling asleep at about 4:00 A.M. in utter exhaustion. By 6:30 his father was shaking him awake, warning him he could not be late today of all days.

At eight o'clock that morning he had been at the *lycée*, seated in the large room with about four hundred other students. Most of them, like Jean-Marc, were bleary-eyed from lack of sleep; but the tension of the hour pumped adrenalin through their veins, giving them an unusual alertness, considering the lack of sleep and the collective fatigue of countless hours of study and preparation.

They were about to take the final test, the baccalaureate exam that would determine who would be accepted into the university. Jean-Marc knew that only half of the students in the room were likely to pass. Passing the "bac" was the key

People boarding crowded bus in Dakar, Senegal

to a successful future in West Africa. A university degree was *everything*. Passing the "bac" was *the* key to entering the university.

For eight hours, Jean-Marc and the other students in the room had concentrated with fierce intensity, trying to recall everything they had learned in *collège* (grammar school) and then *lycée*. To say it was difficult would be an understatement. It was the most demanding, mind-boggling, arduous examination Jean-Marc or any of the other students had ever taken in their entire lives. It covered everything: physics, chemistry, biology, geology, geochemistry, environmental studies, economics, algebra, calculus, geometry, statistics, anthropology, philosophy, psychology, religion, political science, African and French literature, African and French

history, French language, music—and on and on the compre-
hensive tests continued.

At five o'clock in the afternoon the final bell had rung, forc-
ing Jean-Marc and the other students to turn in their examination papers whether they had finished or not. There were a
number of questions Jean-Marc left unanswered, either
because he didn't know the answers or did not have time to
finish. He had hoped to come back to the ones he didn't know
and guess an answer, but time had run out.

Exhausted and drained physically, mentally, and emotionally, Jean-Marc had left the *lycée* and walked several blocks
to a street vendor, where he bought some fish stew and rice
for his evening meal. He had tried to relax while he ate, but he
was so keyed up and so worried about the final results that he
had difficulty unwinding. While he was eating, it started to
rain.

He had waited for the rain to slacken, but it seemed to rain
even harder. He was tempted to sit and wait it out, but a
stronger desire pushed him onward despite his exhaustion.
His day was not over yet. He didn't want to be late to his last
TEE class of the year, even though it came immediately after
the roughest examination he'd ever taken.

Out into the rain he had run, heading for the bus stop. As
he ran, those two words kept pounding his brain when his
feet pounded the sloshing pavement: *étudier . . . s'appliquer
. . . étudier . . . s'appliquer.*

Even though he reached the bus stop in time, there was a
10-minute wait, not unusual during rainy season. Finally
Jean-Marc was on board and headed toward the *Centre Baptiste* in the *Ouagou Niayes* section for his TEE class.

While water dripped from his soaked clothes to the floor of
the bus, Jean-Marc hung precariously onto the hand strap in
the standing-room-only aisle of the crowded bus. As he rode
down the *Boulevard du Général de Gaulle,* Jean-Marc reflected on the intensity of his study during the past year.

He had taken his first Theological Education by Extension
course in September, meeting weekly with Paul Grossman
for six months for the most intensive Bible study he had ever

experienced. At the same time he was also completing the last five of the courses in the Baptist Correspondence School under the supervision of Sally Cawthon.

Jean-Marc had understood her advice not to try to complete the courses so quickly, but he was consumed by a passion to know more and more about the Bible. He wanted to learn as quickly as he could as much as he could.

But as Sally Cawthon predicted, his grades had suffered. He made a C on each of the five correspondence courses and barely squeaked by with a C in his first TEE course. Even worse, he had trouble with several courses at the *lycée* because he was studying harder for the correspondence courses and the TEE class than he was for them.

Jean-Marc might as well have stayed home and rested that night after his "bac" exam. Even though he was present physically, he was so drained mentally and emotionally from the pressure of the day he was really "out of it." His mind drifted in and out, and once when Grossman directed a question to him, Jean-Marc stared off into space in a trance-like stupor, totally unaware that he had been addressed.

The missionary shook his head in dismay. Grossman knew Jean-Marc wanted to learn, but he did poorly on every test and gave every evidence that he did not adequately study.

"Jean-Marc. Jean-Marc. Jean-Marc!"

Three times, each time louder than before, Grossman called before the trance was broken.

"What's wrong, son?" the missionary asked.

"Oh, nothing," Jean-Marc replied. He didn't share with the missionary the tremendous pressure he had faced that day or what was really troubling him.

II

Jean-Marc dreaded what faced him more than any other trial he had experienced in his life. All afternoon he had wandered along the streets of Dakar, trying to think of the best way to handle the situation. He had prayed for guidance, but there were no flashes of inspiration.

That night during the evening meal, he was uneasy and nervous, saying little and trying to act cheerful. But it was a false act, and he knew it. He only hoped Zukono and Narie would not notice how distraught he was.

But they did. Finally Zukono asked him bluntly:

"What's troubling you, son?"

"Oh, it's nothing, father."

"But I can tell something is wrong," Zukono observed. "What is it?"

"I'm just tired, father. It's been a tough year, and I'm just tired.

The moment the words slipped from his lips, Jean-Marc knew he had said the wrong thing. He should never have mentioned that it had been a "tough" year.

Zukono picked up the signal immediately and asked the dreaded question.

"Have you heard how you ranked on the baccalaureate exam?"

Jean-Marc didn't know what to say, so he just dropped his chin to his chest and looked down at the almost-full plate of food he had hardly touched. For several moments he sat in silence. In a voice almost inaudible, he muttered into his plate: "I passed."

"What did you say?" demanded Zukono.

"I passed," Jean-Marc said louder. Then looking into his father's face, he blurted, "I passed the 'bac,' but I don't want to go the university!"

With a fury that frightened the entire family, Zukono rose, knocking over the glass of beer he was drinking with his meal. "What do you mean?" he demanded. "Of course you are going to the university!"

Jean-Marc was silent. He knew nothing he could say would calm his father's anger and frustration.

Standing in front of the table, his eyes flashing with rage, Zukono lashed out at his son again. "Without a university degree you'll never be the success I've wanted you to be. I've sacrificed everything for you to get an education, and you say you aren't going to the university. How could you talk that way?"

Silence. Then a meek "I'm sorry I've disappointed you."

It wasn't enough. Being sorry did not restore Zukono's shattered dreams. It did not change reality.

While Zukono ranted and raved, Narie, Rama, Seynabou, and Moussa sat at the table in silence, afraid even to move. They had all seen and felt the strong man's wrath when he lost his temper. But they also believed Zukono would never beat Jean-Marc because he was the favorite son—the only full-blooded Fon son of the family. They were all jealous of that favored position.

"I can't believe it," Zukono lamented again. "How could you choose not to go the university? Why?"

"I appreciate my education, father," Jean-Marc replied. "Of the 413 students who took the test, only 176 passed. I'm grateful and proud."

"Then what are you talking about?" Zukono snapped back in reply. "I was afraid you wouldn't pass because you spent so many nights studying those Bible correspondence courses and attending the theological classes at the center. But Gou helped you in spite of your foolishness. Now you must continue your education."

"But, father," Jean-Marc interjected, "maybe God does not want me to go to the university. I've been thinking a lot about it."

"How could you even think that?" Zukono answered. "A university degree is the passport to success here. You know that. Without it, you are nothing."

"Father, I've wanted to tell you this for a long time but have not had the courage," Jean-Marc said. "I want to go to the Baptist School of Theology for West Africa in Lomé, Togo."

The words hit Zukono with the power of a sledgehammer. His head jerked and his face turned pale. "Why?" he asked. "Why would you want to go to Lomé to study theology?"

"Father, you remember the nightmare I had about Pierre's death? Ever since then I've felt more and more that God was leading me to be a missionary to Pierre's people to fulfill Pierre's dream. Now I am sure of it. But to achieve that goal, I need more theological education, more intense study of the Bible."

Zukono sat back down at the table. He looked crushed, his dreams deflated. When he sat down, Narie took the cue and said quietly to the younger children, "Let's go to the other room so your father and Jean-Marc can talk." They all knew this was a matter only father and son could settle.

"Oh, Amasou," his father lamented. "I've had such high hopes for you. I've made such sacrifices so you could get a university education. I so much wanted you to return to our homeland as a successful government leader. Now all that I've worked for and dreamed for seems to be vanishing, blowing away like the dust on the streets of Dakar."

Jean-Marc arose from his chair and walked over to his father's side. Tenderly he put his arm around his father's shoulder to console him. "Father, you have not failed, and neither have I. It is my *fa*, my destiny. It is what God wants for my life, what is best for me and, ultimately, for you. Both of us are successes because we are fulfilling our *fa*, our destiny. God has a plan and a purpose for your life, just as he has for mine. Our major goal should be to try to find God's will and fulfill the destiny he has planned for us."

Abruptly Zukono shrugged off Jean-Marc's comforting hand from his shoulder and quickly stood up. His eyes flashed with anger, and his teeth gnashed together as he sought to restrain his strong arms. His piercing eyes lashed at Jean-Marc, but he said not a word. With more anger than Jean-Marc had ever seen before, his father rushed out the door and into the night. Jean-Marc knew where he was going. He would be drunk within an hour.

III

Upset and discouraged after the confrontation with his father, Jean-Marc walked outside to sit under the baobab tree. Fortunately, it wasn't raining. The sky was clear, and the stars were twinkling overhead. Stars seemed to shine only during the rainy season because dust and haze in the atmosphere often blocked them from view during the dry season. But the rains washed away the sky like giant wiper-blades cleaning the windows to the heavens.

The courtyard was full of children from the neighboring apartments, running and playing in the muggy night air. There must have been 20 children playing under the baobab.

Jean-Marc wanted to be alone, and he didn't want to be at home when his father returned from his predictable drunken spree. He didn't fear his father's violent temper; he just wanted to avoid further confrontation.

He walked up the dusty alley, turned onto the *Avenue de la Liberté* and waited at the bus stop, just as he had done every morning for years. He took the first bus that came along and noticed that it was headed for the *Route de la Corniche*, which followed the beach toward the university. It was the same bus he had taken 18 months ago, the morning after his confrontation with Zukono following the horrible nightmare about the death of Pierre.

Jean-Marc got off the bus at the same park, walked out on the beach, and sat under the same palm tree. He looked out over the roaring waves and up into the star-studded heavens, once again feeling the peaceful presence of God.

In the quietness and solitude of the moment, Jean-Marc prayed. "Lord, thank you for the experiences you have given me during these past 18 months. I praise your name for what you have done in my life. I give thanks for the knowledge and the understanding of your Word that you have given me. I thank you for the insight and the counsel you have provided through brothers and sisters in Christ. Lord, thank you for the life and witness of my best friend, Pierre, and for revealing to me through him that you are truly God of this beautiful universe, and Savior of all who will trust your Son.

"Lord, you've blessed me more than I deserve. When I've been unworthy, you've been in control of my life and have used even the bad experiences to teach me your truth. So, take my life and use it, Lord. It isn't much.

"Forgive me, Lord, when I fail you—when I am less than you created me to be. And thank you, Lord, for changing my life. Thank you for forgiving the sin that so controlled my life before you came into my heart.

"Lord, I pray for my father, that somehow I might be able to lead him to trust in you. Right now I know my father is somewhere getting drunk. Help him to realize that drinking is no solution to the problems of life. Help him to understand why I so much want to follow your will and to be a missionary to Pierre's people. And Lord, if he can't understand or accept that, I pray that somehow you might open his mind so that he will not disown me from the family. Help him to realize he has not failed.

"And Father, I pray that somehow you will open the way for me to attend the Baptist School of Theology for West Africa in Lomé. Lord, I don't know how I can possibly raise the money to pay my way through this school, but I trust you to provide the way if that's what you want me to do."

On and on he prayed, for more than an hour. Jean-Marc poured out his soul to God that night, trusting completely in him for guidance and direction in the future.

When he said amen, Jean-Marc was filled with a peace and quiet comfort that exceeded anything he had experienced before in his pilgrimage as a Christian. He knew what he wanted to do next.

CLEARING THE WAY

I

The next morning Jean-Marc awoke to the sound of Narie shouting at Zukono. No matter what she did, however, Zukono would not awaken. He was in such a drunken stupor that nothing would rouse him. Narie feared he might lose his job at the nail factory if he didn't get up. Jean-Marc dressed quietly, anxious not to become involved in Narie's frustration because he knew nothing he could do would help matters at that time. He went immediately to *Centre Baptiste,* where he poured out his soul to Diatta about his experiences. Diatta had been the first person Jean-Marc told about his decision to try to enter the Baptist School of Theology for West Africa and Diatta was the first person he sought after the latest confrontation with Zukono.

When Jean-Marc expressed his fear that Zukono might disown him if he went to Lomé against his wishes, Diatta expressed his doubt that this would happen. "Remember, you are his only full-blooded Fon son, a surviving twin. Zukono might be angry with you, but he will never disown you," Diatta said.

Diatta understood how Zukono felt, but he encouraged Jean-Marc to continue on his course if he remained convinced that God wanted him to pursue his theological education.

He encouraged Jean-Marc to talk with Pastor Runyan, who had just returned from a year's furlough in the United States in time to attend the annual meeting of the Senegal Baptist Mission. Diatta said Runyan would be coming by the center later in the morning on his way to the mission meeting scheduled to start that afternoon. With nothing else to do, Jean-Marc waited for Runyan to return.

When he walked in the door, Farrell Runyan seemed overjoyed to see Jean-Marc. He was even more excited when Jean-Marc began to share with him all that had happened in his life while the missionary had been away. He told him not only about his quest for knowledge and understanding of the Bible but of the dream and vision that led him to believe God was calling him to be a missionary to the people of Timbuktu. Runyan seemed genuinely pleased that Jean-Marc wanted to attend the "pastors' school" (as most of the missionaries called the Baptist School of Theology for West Africa) in Lomé.

Pastor Runyan agreed with Diatta that Zukono would not disown Jean-Marc if he went to the school in Lomé. When

Jean-Marc shared his apprehension about financing his education without Zukono's support, Runyan responded exactly as Jean-Marc thought he would.

"If it is really God's will for you to attend the pastors' school, somehow God will provide the way for you to do it." The missionary didn't say so, but he already had an idea.

Even though Jean-Marc emphatically stated his desire to go to Timbuktu to proclaim the gospel to the Songhai people, Runyan encouraged him to consider returning to Senegal to become the first national pastor of a Senegalese Baptist church. Although no congregation in Senegal was strong enough financially now to support a full-time pastor, there was a rapidly growing congregation in the Casamance region of Senegal that might be strong enough to support a bivocational pastor within a few years.

"But I'm not Senegalese; I am Fon," Jean-Marc pointed out. "To be really effective, the pastor of the congregation in Bignona needs to speak Diola as Diatta does."

Even though Diatta had expressed interest in becoming a pastor and had taken the first two TEE courses, he had not said specifically that God had called him to the ministry, nor that God wanted him to attend the school of theology in Lomé. Since he was a married man with children, attendance at the pastors' school would be more difficult for Diatta.

For more than an hour, Jean-Marc shared his hopes and dreams with Farrell Runyan and Diatta. Runyan seemed more relaxed than before. He had seemed always in a hurry before his furlough. This time it was Diatta who had to break up the conversation, insisting that Runyan leave so he would not be late to the mission meeting. Even then, he didn't rush off in a cloud of dust. Before leaving he asked Diatta and Jean-Marc to join him in the courtyard to pray for Jean-Marc and for the mission meeting. They parted on a high note of hope for the future.

II

Fortunately, Jean-Marc never learned all that happened at the mission meeting that followed. He would have been horrified to know that his desire to attend the school in Lomé was the cause of disagreement among the missionaries.

In his quiet, gentle way, Ken Robertson presided over the annual meeting of the Senegal Baptist Mission. Assigned to Bignona in the Casamance region, he was mission chairman for the year. He expected some debate because they were to discuss the annual budget. All missionaries needed more money for their work; consequently, they had different priorities. But in spite of their different needs they were usually able to come to some agreement.

When Farrell Runyan presented his unanticipated motion, an unusually heated debate arose. Coming to the meeting fresh from his session with Jean-Marc, Runyan shared with the other missionaries very briefly what Jean-Marc had told him and then presented a motion that was not on the agenda.

"I move," he said, "that the Senegal Baptist Mission sponsor Jean-Marc as the first full-time student at the Baptist School of Theology for West Africa in Lomé, and that we approve the transfer of $2,000 from the funds allocated in next year's budget for repair and maintenance of the air conditioner at the mission office to set up a scholarship fund for Jean-Marc."

The group was taken by surprise. Frank Cawthon, the mission treasurer, was the first to respond. Even though he expressed strong personal support for Jean-Marc and the desire to do everything possible to help him attend the pastors' school, Cawthon was strongly opposed to the motion for several reasons.

"As business manager, I'm the guy who gets caught in the squeeze when the unexpected happens," he said. "The air conditioner at the mission office is on its last leg, and it's liable to go out at any time. We must budget for the repairs next year. Otherwise, if the air conditioner goes out, we will end up voting in Executive Committee to take the money from some other account to make the needed repairs, or even worse, to overspend the budget. I just don't think it is good business to approve a motion like this on the spur of the moment without adequate study and evaluation."

Runyan was quick to defend his point. "We don't know that the air conditioner is going to break down. It could last not only next year but the year after without repairs. Even if it does break down, we might have to go for months without it before we can find the parts to repair it. We'll just have to open the windows and be hot. I believe that people are more important than machines and that training future pastors is more important than air conditioning.

Paul Grossman opposed the motion from another stand-point. "I've been teaching Jean-Marc in the TEE classes all this year, and I am not sure he is the caliber of theology student who can make it at the pastors' school. You know it will be tougher on him than the correspondence courses and the TEE classes; to be honest with you, I've been stretching the point to give him the two C's. I've seen his records on the correspondence courses, and he hasn't made anything higher than a C on any of them. I just don't think he has the academic qualities to make it as a theology student."

Sally Cawthon couldn't let the last remark go by without contesting it. "It's true that Jean-Marc's grades aren't high. But you must realize what tremendous pressure he has been under this past year. He's faced opposition at home. He's carried the toughest load at the *lycée* he's ever carried. And on top of the pressure to pass the 'bac' to gain admission to the university, he has taken five correspondence courses and two TEE courses during the last 12 months. It's no wonder his grades are barely C's. I doubt that you could have done any better yourself, Paul."

Runyan added: "Today I had a long talk with both Jean-Marc and Diatta. I'm convinced that he overextended himself and tried to do too much. If he were a full-time student at the pastors' school, he could devote himself completely to theological studies. I believe he is so highly motivated that he would excel if given the opportunity.

"Also, it's important to know that Diatta has an extremely high regard for Jean-Marc's potential as a pastor. I'll never forget something that John Mills (area director for West Africa at the Foreign Mission Board and former missionary to

West Africa) once said: 'A white man can never really judge the potential of an African. Only another African can do that.' I trust Diatta's evaluation of Jean-Marc a lot more than yours, Paul."

Peggy Grossman spoke up. "I want to bring up a point that nobody else has even mentioned. What if we do send Jean-Marc to Lomé? We'd be depriving ourselves of a national Baptist leader; we'd have no assurance whatever that he would return to Senegal to help with our churches. Indeed, he has stated clearly that his dream is to go to Mali as a missionary to Timbuktu. We don't have any Southern Baptist work in Mali, and the chances of his being able to start work in a predominantly Muslim society like Timbuktu without the resources of a mission backing him are next to nothing. Even if he doesn't fail in Lomé, he's likely to fail in Mali, and we would be losing one of our best leaders. I've heard the missionaries in Ivory Coast and Ghana complain because they have sent some of their young pastors to Lomé, and the men did not return to their countries. I'd much rather see Jean-Marc stay in Dakar, continue with the TEE study, and help us with our centers and churches here."

Frank Cawthon disagreed. "That's pretty selfish for us. You're saying in essence, 'We don't want to give up one of our leaders to do missions work in Mali.' Actually, we ought to rejoice that God has called Jean-Marc to start work in Mali because we Southern Baptists may never be able to enter Mali. To argue that he is doomed to failure is too pessimistic. If the Lord is leading Jean-Marc to Mali, then the Lord will lead him in winning the people. He cannot fail if God is with him. He's bound to have as much success there as we have here in Senegal, and that's not saying much. I can't support the motion, but I surely do support Jean-Marc and believe he is earnestly seeking God's will. It would be wrong for us to believe otherwise and to stand in his way because of our own selfish attitudes."

Pointing out that only Runyan, the Cawthons, and the Grossmans had spoken, Robertson asked the other missionaries to voice their views.

Only Tomé Halsell, now serving in Hong Kong but at that time student worker at the University of Dakar, supported the motion. He reiterated Runyan's emphasis that people are more important than the comfort of an air conditioner.

Everett Burnette, at that time assigned to the Casamance region, opposed the motion. "I don't know Jean-Marc and so speak objectively. I feel we would set a dangerous precedent. If we provide a scholarship for the first student who wants to go to the pastors' school, every other student who wants to go will expect a scholarship too. We just can't afford to get into the scholarship business."

Everyone else remained silent, apparently uncommitted. When the vote was taken, there were six yeas and seven nays. Jean-Marc's hopes for a scholarship died before they even had a chance to be born.

III

Its wheels spinning in the deep sand, the white car fought to keep from getting stuck, finally gripping more solid ground. It stopped in the narrow alley in front of Zukono's house, and Farrell Runyan stepped out. He clapped his hand outside the door of Jean-Marc's house, awakening him from his afternoon *sieste.*

Together they walked under the baobab tree to chat. It was an unexpected visit, the first time Runyan had ever come to see Jean-Marc at his home. For several minutes they went through the formalities of greeting before Runyan abruptly announced the point of his visit.

"Jean-Marc, are you still convinced that God is leading you to enter the Baptist School of Theology for West Africa in Lomé?"

When Jean-Marc said yes, Runyan gave him some unexpected good news. "Today I received a letter from a wealthy Baptist layman in the States saying that he felt God was leading him to help some worthy young pastor get started in the ministry. I believe the letter is God's answer to your prayers. If you still want to go to the pastors' school in September, I'll be glad to write the layman, tell him of your needs, and see if he would like to provide you a scholarship."

Jean-Marc was so excited he wanted to shout for joy. But in typical African style, he hesitated to show his true feelings, especially to a *toubob*. Even though Jean-Marc had come to a new appreciation for the Baptist missionaries, he still felt uneasy about expressing his true feelings to them.

When he assured Pastor Runyan that he did indeed believe this was the answer to his prayers, Runyan pointed out that there were still many details that would have to be worked out. He would have to write to William McCall, the president of the theological school, and send him transcripts of Jean-Marc's record from the TEE classes. "Normally, they require two years of TEE study before they will accept a new student, but I know they have made exceptions in the past and with your baccalaureate certificate, I believe they will in your case," Runyan said. "If you are accepted and if the layman agrees to help, we will set up a scholarship fund for you. We can't expect to cover all your expenses, especially your transportation from Dakar to Lomé, however."

Jean-Marc was so excited that he could hardly speak. He didn't know what to say. All he could think of was, "*Merci beaucoup* (thank you)." Over and over, he repeated the same phrase.

Then Runyan cautioned Jean-Marc not to tell anyone about the scholarship. "Let's just wait and see if it all works out before we tell anyone. I've also got an idea on how you might be able to travel cheaply to Togo. Dakar is a major port, and there are frequent cargo ships that unload part of their freight here in Dakar and ship the remainder of their load to other French West Africa ports such as Abidjan and Lomé. Maybe we can find a freighter that needs a crew member, and you could work your way down to Lomé."

Although he had never been on a ship before, Jean-Marc liked the idea. He asked Pastor Runyan to help him find out if such a vacancy might exist on the crew of any of the ships that might dock between then and September in Dakar.

A month passed. Finally, letters arrived within a week from

Lomé and from Amarillo, Texas, both bringing good news. The layman in Texas agreed to the scholarship, and William McCall indicated Jean-Marc's acceptance as a student for the fall semester of the Baptist school in Lomé.

Within another week, Runyan had located a freighter whose cook had been thrown in jail for stabbing a man in a brawl. Runyan knew that Jean-Marc had once worked for several weeks as a cook in a Dakar hotel, filling in for a friend at the *lycée* who was in the hospital. He hoped Jean-Marc had learned enough in those three weeks to qualify for the position.

With only two weeks to prepare for his departure, Jean-Marc was pushed to get ready. What he dreaded was breaking the news to Zukono. He knew what reaction to expect, and he feared the worst.

Harbor and docks, Dakar, Senegal

part two

Love in Lomé

JOURNEY TO ABIDJAN

WHEN JEAN-MARC TOLD HIS FATHER that he had made definite plans to attend the Baptist School of Theology for West Africa in Lomé, Togo, he was not prepared for Zukono's response.

With dread and fear in his heart, Jean-Marc had approached his father after the evening meal the day he heard from Pastor Runyan that he had been accepted at the school and that he had gotten the job as a cook's helper. The ship, Esprit de Liberté, on which he had the job, was leaving the next week for Abidjan and Lomé.

"Father, I received some exciting news today. I'm so happy that I can hardly contain myself. And I want to share my joy and happiness with you."

Zukono looked at his son with his piercing eyes and merely grunted.

View of Gorée Island from Dakar, Senegal

"I've been accepted as a student at the Baptist School of Theology in Lomé, Togo, with a full scholarship, and Pastor Runyan has made arrangements for me to get a job working as a cook's helper on a French freighter bound from Dakar to Abidjan and then on to Lomé." Jean-Marc said it all in one breath, quickly blurting out the news with excitement.

Silence followed his announcement. Zukono said nothing. He stared at Jean-Marc, dropped his eyes to the table for a few moments, then looked out into space with a faraway stare. But he said not a word.

Jean-Marc was stunned. He expected outrage, a diatribe, a stormy argument. But Zukono just sat there, staring into space.

"Father, did you hear what I said?"

Silence again. After a moment, Zukono softly reponded. His voice was full of disappointment and sadness. "I heard. It is no surprise. I knew this was coming. The only news is that you have found a way to travel to Lomé without asking me for money to pay your expenses. Even the scholarship is no surprise."

Jean-Marc pulled his chair around in order to sit directly in his father's line of sight as he stared off into space. The spell broken, Zukono looked at his son, grief and pain streaming from the wrinkles in his face.

"Father, I would not ask you for money to pay for my Christian education, for I know you do not approve. I will find a way to pay for my education. It is something I feel compelled to do. I don't ask for your approval or blessing; I only ask that you continue to love me as your son, for that can never change."

Silence again. Glassy eyes stared out into space. Then the eyes blinked, and a tear trickled down the wrinkled black face. Zukono's heart melted into tenderness.

"I do love you, Amasou," he said. "That's what hurts so much. I had such great dreams for you. I wanted you to fulfill the desires I had for myself but I could never achieve because of my lack of education. I know I cannot live your life for you, but I wanted so much for you to share my hopes and dreams.

You will always be my son, though, my only Fon son."

Zukono paused for a moment and then continued. "Wait here, my son. There is something I want you to have."

He got up and walked into his bedroom, leaving Jean-Marc alone in the outer room. Narie and the children had gone outside following the evening meal to fetch some water and play. In a few minutes, Zukono returned carrying a bundle wrapped in a protective cloth.

He set the bundle on the table and gingerly unwrapped the contents. "I have two gifts for you that mean a great deal to me. I want you to have them to take to Lomé when you go."

He presented to Jean-Marc a wooden carving of a male doll about five inches tall. Jean-Marc recognized it immediately, recalling his childhood days when he played with the doll constantly.

Called a *hoho,* the doll represented the image of his dead twin brother. Zukono believed that the spirit of Jean-Marc's twin lived in the wooden doll. The Fon belief was that the spirits of twins could never be separated.

"This is for you," Zukono said. "You must take it with you because you are special, Amasou. You are a twin, and you must never separate from the spirit of your twin brother."

Before Jean-Marc could respond, Zukono pulled from the bundle the second item. It was the horn of a large antelope, with a strip of white cloth about two inches wide wrapped around the base of the antelope horn. Attached to the cloth and the horn were five small pieces of iron and several beads. Beneath the white piece of cloth were bits of herbs and medicines.

"This *gbo* (fetish) was given to me by the old priest in Gomé, the village where I was reared, just before I left on the trip to Dakar," Zukono said. "It is called an *agbanli,* and it will protect you from harm on your trip. As long as you carry this, nothing can hurt you on your journey. One of the five pieces of iron on the outside is called 'Zu,' which means 'hammer'; it will drive away all evil. Take it, Amasou, to protect you on your journey."

Jean-Marc at first did not know how to respond because he

knew how deeply his father treasured these two sacred fetishes. He did not want to offend his father, who had received the news of his decision far more graciously than Jean-Marc had expected. But he did not believe in fetishes, and he wanted nothing to do with them. Suddenly he had an idea.

"Father, I thank you for wanting to give to me these things you treasure so much, but I cannot accept them for three reasons. First, I want you to keep the *hoho* as a constant reminder that my spirit is with you. It will mean more to you than it would to me. Second, I want you to keep the *agbanli* because you might want to take a trip while I am gone and you would not want to leave without it. But third, and most important of all, these things are sacred to you.

"Father, I have learned to trust in Jesus completely. I believe he is stronger and more powerful than any object made by a fetish priest. It would be hypocritical of me to take these things with me when they mean much to you, not me, father. I want you to keep them."

Zukono continued his sad stare into space for a few moments. Then, much to Jean-Marc's surprise, Zukono's lips turned upward in a smile so slight it was hardly perceptible. Jean-Marc knew that he had said the right thing. Now he could leave with peace in his heart.

II

The awesome size of the freighter, *Esprit de Liberté* overwhelmed Jean-Marc. He couldn't believe how gigantic the freighter was.

He was glad his job was that of cook's helper rather than cook, as he had first believed. André, the cook, was a big, burly Ivorian of the Baoulé tribe. He was a jovial fellow who seemed to enjoy eating as much as he did cooking. But there was a tough side to him too, and Jean-Marc realized quickly he had better not do anything to upset his new boss.

Jean-Marc was amazed not only at the size of the ship, but at the cargo it was carrying. The entire ship was filled with grocery items from Europe that were being shipped to stock the supermarkets that catered to the wealthy Africans and the Europeans living in Dakar, Abidjan, and Lomé. He was not allowed to go into the hold where these grocery items were stored, but he heard the cook talk about the gourmet foods fit for a king that were on the ship but not served to the crew.

When the ship weighed anchor, Jean-Marc looked out over the harbor of Dakar with sadness. Although he wanted to go to Lomé more than anything in the world, he didn't want to leave home. He thought of his father and how much he loved him. He wished that somehow his father could understand how deep that love was, even though Jean-Marc also wanted to fulfill the calling that he felt so deeply.

As the ship's powerful screws began to turn, Jean-Marc looked over the rail and realized what a significant moment this was in his life. Nothing would ever be the same again. He might return to Dakar, but in essence he was leaving the only home he could remember. How he wished his father had gone to the docks with him so he could wave good-bye one final time. But Zukono had gone to work that day, just as any other day. Jean-Marc was fairly certain that his father refused to come to the docks because he could not endure the emotional trauma of seeing his only Fon son sail away.

Looking out over the beautiful natural harbor of Dakar, Jean-Marc watched closely as the ship churned past Gorée Island. He regretted that he had never gone to the island to see for himself the place about which he had heard many strange stories. Some Senegalese refused to set foot on the island. They believed it was haunted by the spirits of thousands of slaves who died on the island rather than board the slave trading ships anchored in the harbor.

Jean-Marc had heard stories told by the *griots*, the traditional storytellers and historians of the Senegalese people, about the horrors of Gorée Island. From the 1500s to the 1800s, Gorée Island was one of the key shipping points in the African slave trade. First controlled by the Portuguese and later by the Dutch, English, and French, the island was the holding point where thousands of slaves were imprisoned. There they were retained until slave trader ships loaded them like cordwood into dark holds of filthy, three-masted ships before sailing to the West Indies and on to America. Many of these slaves were Fon who were captured by the Yoruba and the Ouidah, their traditional enemies from lands to the south and west, southern Benin and Nigeria.

Jean-Marc felt sick at his stomach as he thought of the indignities suffered by his forefathers, not only because of slavery, but also because of colonialism. Although Jean-Marc felt he harbored no prejudice or hatred toward the *toubob,* and especially toward the French, he could understand why other Africans did hate the *toubob* generally. But Jean-Marc was different. He was a Christian, and he had come to know and to love many white men who were gracious, caring people who loved the Africans and wanted to help them. He did feel, though, that many Americans, and even more French, were paternalistic and condescending in their attitudes toward the Africans. They seemed to feel that the French way or the American way was always the *best* way, and that the African way was somehow inferior.

As he thought about the people who meant the most to him —his father, Diatta, and the missionaries—Jean-Marc felt homesick even before he was out of sight of the Dakar harbor. There was a dull ache in the pit of his stomach. He tried to cheer himself up with the thought that he was doing what God wanted him to do and that he should be happy and excited about the future.

But he felt only sadness and a sense of loss as he watched the beautiful peninsula fade into the horizon. Now he could understand why the early European explorers had named the pencil-thin peninsula "Cape Verde," which means "green point," for the land from a distance appeared green and beautiful. The end of the rainy season was near, and it was the only time of year that the land was so green and beautiful. Jean-Marc was glad that his last view of Cape Verde was during the time of year that fed his memory with such beauty.

After Jean-Marc watched the coastline disappear behind

the horizon, he left the rail on the poop deck and headed to the galley for his responsibilities for the evening meal. He struggled to climb the companionway leading to the passageway between decks. Already the ship was into the rough waves of the Atlantic, and Jean-Marc lost his footing several times on the west passageway. By the time he got amidships where the galley was, he was beginning to have doubts about the wisdom of working his way to Lomé. He'd never been aboard a ship before, and he didn't like it. He felt crowded, and the narrow passageway gave him claustrophobia. These feelings intensified his homesickness.

When he reached the cook's mess, Jean-Marc felt terrrible. His stomach was churning as if the ship's powerful propellers were twisting like an egg-beater inside him. He tried to keep André from knowing he felt sick, and went straight to work peeling the potatoes as the cook had instructed him. But as Jean-Marc worked, his face turned pasty. Suddenly he couldn't hold his insides any longer. He ran to the door and barely made it before he vomited. The cook cursed. He knew immediately what was wrong. The landlubber was seasick.

Jean-Marc thought he was going to die and even wanted to while he waited for the ship's doctor in sick bay to give him the standard medication. Jean-Marc prayed for relief, but he only felt worse. He was too sick even to stand, and he didn't know how he would make it from sick bay to his quarters. The doctor merely laughed and assured Jean-Marc that he would feel fine by morning. But to Jean-Marc, it was not a laughing matter. He feared that his journey had gotten off to a miserable start. He dreaded the future if this was a foretaste of what was yet to come.

III

When the *Esprit de Liberté* steamed into port at Abidjan, Jean-Marc could hardly believe his eyes. He'd never seen such a beautiful city in all his life. Gleaming white skyscrapers towered into the heavens, taller than any building he'd ever known existed. Huge cranes everywhere

Skyline of Abidjan, Ivory Coast

indicated more skyscrapers were going up. The city perched atop a beautiful peninsula called the Plateau that jutted into the calm waters of the Ebrié Lagoon. Protection from the surf of the ocean came from Boulay Islands.

As the ship sailed slowly past the industrial zones into the *Baie du Banco* adjacent to the tall skyscrapers on the Plateau, Jean-Marc was astounded at the size of the port and the number of ships. He counted at least 35 freighters at the docks. The port seemed even bigger than the one at Dakar. Ships laden with huge logs were everywhere. Jean-Marc assumed that Abidjan was a heavy exporter of lumber.

After the ship docked, Jean-Marc took a bus down the Highway of West Africa, across the Ebrié Lagoon on the Houphou Bridge on to the market in Treichville. Before he left Dakar, Zukono had told him of a kinsman who lived some-where in the Marcory section of Abidjan. At the port someone

told Jean-Marc the best way to find him was to go to the Treichville market and look for the Fon traders who worked there.

At the Treichville market Jean-Marc easily found several Fon traders by listening for the familiar sound of his native tongue. But no one knew Dosu, his kinsman. They suggested he go to some shops along Marcory Avenue, where some other Fon traders lived. But after he took the bus there, he could find no one who knew Dosu. Jean-Marc had hoped to stay at his kinsman's home during the two weeks that his ship would be docked in Abidjan.

Jean-Marc began to wander aimlessly down the streets of the Marcory section. He didn't know where to turn or anyone who might help him. He knew there were Baptist missionaries in Abidjan, but he didn't know where they lived or how to contact them. He was tired and discouraged, but most of all, his jaw ached and throbbed. One of his lower jaw teeth was hurting so badly that it sent shooting pains not only into his jaw but into his neck and back.

As he turned a corner heading toward an unknown destiny, Jean-Marc suddenly saw a sign that sparked excitement and hope. The sign said *Eglise Baptiste Protestante.* Jean-Marc opened the gate leading to the church compound and shouted in French, asking if anyone was there. A thin young man with a moustache came outside and greeted him. When the young man introduced himself as Gueye Brice, pastor of the church, Jean-Marc almost shouted with joy. He could hardly believe that such a young man could be pastor of such a big church, one wealthy enough to afford its own building. When Brice learned that Jean-Marc was a Baptist from Dakar who was on a journey to Lomé to enter the Baptist School of Theology for West Africa, he became almost as excited as Jean-Marc. They sat down under a tree in the church courtyard and began to pepper each other with questions.

Brice and Jean-Marc became friends almost immediately. Like Jean-Marc, Brice wanted theological training, but he was interested in going to a Bible school in France that he had heard about from a friend. For almost two hours, they talked and shared dreams for the future. Jean-Marc was so enthralled that he forgot all about his failure to have a place to stay. Brice brought the subject up by asking Jean-Marc where he was going and why he was in the Marcory section. When Jean-Marc told his story, Brice invited him to spend the night in his apartment there at the church. Jean-Marc enthusiastically accepted his invitation, and the two young men passed the night away discovering the thrilling details of each one's spiritual pilgrimage and dreams for the future.

IV

The next morning Brice invited Jean-Marc to go with him to the Publication Center for French-speaking Africa, and then to visit his office. He was one of the editors for an inter-

Baptist church in Marcory section, Abidjan, Ivory Coast

denominational African magazine called *Tam Tam*. Brice needed to go by the publication center to pick up some material that he was taking to print on the presses where he worked. He explained that the center published literature for all the Baptist churches in French-speaking West Africa, while the place where he worked published literature for sale to churches of other denominations in West Africa. "We try to work together closely and help each other," Brice explained.

Even though Jean-Marc's tooth still throbbed, he enjoyed the walk with Brice to the publication center. The walk took them through the most beautiful residential section Jean-Marc had ever seen.

Upon their arrival Brice introduced him to Mitchell Land, director of the center, who offered to take him on a tour of both the center and the Baptist mission office for the Ivory Coast next door.

Jean-Marc was amazed, almost stunned, by what he saw. He had not imagined that Baptist work was so much more advanced in the Ivory Coast than in Senegal. He could hardly believe that there were more than 35 Baptist churches in Ivory Coast and more than 3,000 baptized believers. He was astounded when he learned there were 24 Southern Baptist missionaries in the Ivory Coast. When he saw the sophisticated typesetting equipment at the publication center, his eyes widened with wonderment. He immediately recognized a stack of books that he had read. Land explained that the Baptist Correspondence Course study books for all of Francophone Africa were produced there and distributed to the correspondence course directors and students in the various countries.

While Brice gathered the materials he needed, Mitchell Land took Jean-Marc upstairs and introduced him to Jim Lassiter, the missionary in charge of the audiovisual center. From the sound studio upstairs, Jean-Marc heard the most beautiful African music he'd ever listened to in his life. Lassiter explained that it was a tape of a choir that he and music missionary Jerry Robertson had recorded in the studio. The choir was singing Christian songs written by one of the choir members. Not only was the music beautiful, but the sound system that was playing the recording had the most vibrant, realistic sound he'd ever heard.

Downstairs Lassiter introduced Jean-Marc to Doug Simrell and James Darnell, two of the field evangelists for Ivory Coast Baptist Mission. Darnell explained that he was responsible for helping start new churches and assisting in church development in the cities and villages from the middle of downtown Abidjan north and northwest for about 130 kilometers, while Simrell had those responsibilities in south and southwest Abidjan, including the Marcory section where Brice's church was located. Jean-Marc could hardly believe his ears when Darnell said he worked with about 25 different congregations, some of them churches, some of them small preaching points in the villages.

Simrell stood quietly while Darnell talked on about the challenge of starting new churches and the responsiveness of the people. He had shiny gray hair, and his eyes glistened with enthusiasm as Darnell told Jean-Marc about his work.

Brice arrived, apologizing for the delay. A last-minute correction had been necessary on the material he had come to get.

When Darnell heard where Brice and Jean-Marc were going, he offered to give them a ride. "I'm on my way to take some suppplies out to Dion Robert, the pastor of Yopougon Baptist Church, and I'll be glad to drop you off," he said.

Darnell, Brice, and Jean-Marc walked down a beautiful pathway leading toward the tree-shaded backyard of a big house. While Darnell loaded the literature into the back of his station wagon, Brice and Jean-Marc got inside. They drove across the bridge over the lagoon and entered the most modern freeway Jean-Marc had ever seen. The six-lane, divided highway called the *Boulevard Général de Gaulle* followed the shore of the *Baie de Cocody* on the right and the skyline of the huge buildings of the Plateau on the left. Across the lagoon to the right, Darnell pointed out the *Hôtel Ivoire*, describing it as one of the most beautiful hotels in the world. A few kilometers farther, they turned off the freeway, and

Darnell headed toward Brice's office. Darnell talked the entire route, enthusiastically telling Jean-Marc about his work as a field evangelist.

"I wish you had time to go with me out to the Yopougon Baptist Church," Darnell said to Jean-Marc. "We could drop Brice off, and then you could run out to Yopougon with me. You really need to meet Dion Robert and see the Yopougon church. It's the most exciting church I've ever worked with. I'll tell you what. If you want to run out there with me, I can bring you back after we've finished, and you can spend the rest of the day with Brice. I'm sure he has some work he needs to do anyway."

Jean-Marc agreed and was glad he did. Yopougon church was the most amazing Baptist church he had ever seen. Darnell told him there were more than 600 members, and they were working hard toward constructing a new building. In their present building they could seat only about 255, but they had more than 11 "house churches" scattered throughout the Yopougon area. Dion Robert was the first full-time French-speaking Baptist pastor supported by his church in Ivory Coast, but he wasn't at the church when Jean-Marc and Darnell got there. "He's terribly busy," Darnell explained. He talked on and on about the tremendous potential of the church, explaining that more than 600,000 people will be living in that area within the next few years.

As they drove back, the station wagon hit a deep pothole in the road, and Jean-Marc cried out in pain. His toothache was worse. When Darnell asked what was wrong, Jean-Marc explained. After they stopped, Darnell asked to look at his tooth, whistling in dismay when he saw how bad the infection was. "You need to get this taken care of," he suggested. "I'll tell you what. Tomorrow I am driving my children to Bouaké, where they attend school. We have a Baptist dental clinic up there, and Dr. Charles Deevers, the missionary dentist, can fix that tooth for you. But it's a long, hard drive, and we'll have to leave early.

Jean-Marc was hurting so much that he would have done just about anything to get some relief. He said he'd be grate-

Worship service at Yopougon Baptist Church, Abidjan, Ivory Coast

ful to be able to go. That night he slept fitfully and was up early the next morning.

V

The drive to Bouaké was filled with wonderment for Jean-Marc. He had never before seen country so varied. Part of the trip took them through a rain forest with trees taller than Jean-Marc dreamed possible. Suddenly the tropical forest changed to savannah, with grassy flatlands punctured by an occasional tree. It was a difficult trip, and it was late when they arrived in Bouaké.

The next morning Jean-Marc went to the dental clinic early enough to be there at the 8:00 A.M. opening. Almost 75 peo-

ple were waiting, sitting on benches in a large, open-air portico. One of the seven dental assistants at the clinic gave
Jean-Marc a metal tag with a number on it and Jean-Marc
took a seat with the others.

In a few moments an American missionary with an extremely fair complexion and the blondest hair Jean-Marc had
ever seen came out and began to speak to the people. Two of
the dental assistants stood beside him, translating his French
into Baoulé and Dioula. He introduced himself as Dan
Routledge and told the people that Baptists were operating
the dental clinic not just to meet physical needs but also to
share with people the love of Jesus Christ. Then he introduced the people to Jesus.

Jean-Marc waited about an hour after the message before it
was his turn to see the dentist. He met Dr. Deevers and told
him who he was and why he was in Ivory Coast. A tall, thin
man, Deevers seemed delighted to hear Jean-Marc's story,
asking several questions about how the Lord had called him
to the ministry. Then he looked at the tooth. Jean-Marc
wasn't surprised to learn it was too late to do anything except
pull it.

When the dentist finished the examination, Jean-Marc lay
down on one of the five padded couches in a large treatment
room. Shortly an African who introduced himself as N'Groan
Konon, one of the dental assistants, began to work on his
mouth. First, he gave him an injection to deaden the pain.
Later, he came back and pulled the tooth. All the time, he
talked to Jean-Marc about his love for Jesus, and how his job
as a dental assistant enabled him to show the love of Jesus
through his actions as well as through his words to the patients. He praised both Dr. Deevers and Pastor Routledge, telling Jean-Marc how they had led him to Christ. Routledge had
also helped him start a small chicken farm in his village outside Bouaké.

When Jean-Marc left the clinic, he felt much better both
physically and spiritually. He was excited about what he saw
God doing to reach the people of Bouaké through the dental
clinic.

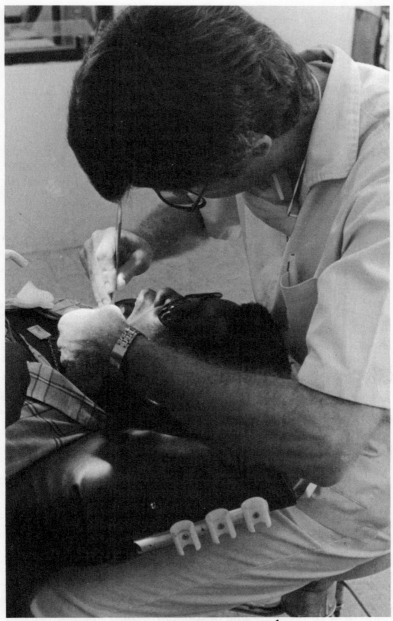
*Missionary Charles Deevers with patient in Bouaké,
Ivory Coast*

On the trip back to Abidjan, Darnell told Jean-Marc about the mission program Southern Baptists sponsor in Ivory Coast. When Jean-Marc expressed amazement that Baptists would use a dental clinic as a means to proclaim the gospel, the missionary pointed out that Baptists thought meeting people's needs was a good way to reach people with the gospel. He explained that in Daloa, about 150 kilometers southwest of Bouaké, agricultural missionary Rod Batie was working closely with field evangelist Ed Pinkston to reach the farmers of the area with the good news and at the same time help the farmers improve farm productivity. In Abidjan, Estelle Freeland was doing social work, with an emphasis on ministering to people who are patients in the big government hospital in the Treichville area.

Jean-Marc returned to Abidjan in awe and wonder at the modern mission methods being used in the Ivory Coast. He wondered what new ideas he would find in Lomé.

VI

Three days before he was to leave Abidjan, Jean-Marc and Brice were walking down the street in the Marcory section when Jean-Marc spotted a church that seemed strange to him. It was a big building, bigger even than the Yopougon church, and much larger than Brice's church. He asked Brice about the sign that read "First Baptist Church of Marcory."

"That's a Yoruba church," Brice said. "We don't really have much to do with that church," he commented.

"Why?" asked Jean-Marc. "What is the relationship between the Yoruba Baptists and the other Baptist churches in Abidjan?"

"Well, you know that Yoruba are rich traders. They're not really Ivorian. They're Nigerian."

"So? It was the Yoruba who invited the Baptist missionaries from the United States to come here to the Ivory Coast to start the French-speaking work, wasn't it?" Jean-Marc asked, recalling one of the many things Pastor Darnell had told him.

"Well, that's true," responded Brice. "The Yoruba churches did invite the missionaries here, but Yorubas themselves and French-speaking Ivorian Baptists don't have much in common. I understand that in Togo and Benin the French-speaking Baptist churches and Yoruba Baptist have more fellowship than they do here. I'll be interested to hear if that's true when you have a chance to get acquainted with the situation in Lomé."

Later, when he was alone, Jean-Marc marveled again at what he'd learned in such a short time. The two weeks in Abidjan had so expanded his understanding of ways to minister to people in the name of Jesus that it was going to be necessary to sit down and sort out what he had learned as soon as possible. He hoped he would have time to write Brice. But if his two years at the Baptist School of Theology for West Africa in Lomé followed the pattern of new experiences of the first leg of his journey, he wondered if he would be able to write even his father.

PREACHING IN LOVE

I

There was no seasickness and little homesickness when Jean-Marc sailed on the *Esprit de Liberté* from Abidjan to Lomé. André was in great spirits after his visit with his family. Jean-Marc felt wonderful, and each night as he prayed and read his Bible, he thanked God for the experiences he had already felt and for what was ahead. He prayed especially for his father, that God's spirit would comfort him and help him feel Jean-Marc's love and concern.

When the ship had docked in Lomé and Jean-Marc was cleared through customs control, he was surprised to see in the hallway a slender, black-haired American wearing glasses. The American held a sign with this name on it, "Zukono Jean-Marc." When Jean-Marc introduced himself, the man with the sign shook his hand warmly and welcomed him to the Republic of Togo.

He was William McCall, the president of the Baptist School of Theology for West Africa. Farrell Runyan had written to him telling him the arrival date of Jean-Marc's ship, and the missionary-educator had come to the docks personally to help Jean-Marc find his way to the school.

From the port area, they drove past sparkling beaches shaded by stately palms, the most beautiful beaches Jean-Marc had ever seen. Then they turned up the *Route d'Atakpamé* and headed across the lagoon to the pastors' school campus. As he drove into the spacious campus, Jean-Marc was impressed with the neat buildings. There was nothing fancy about them, but they were trim and functional.

Missionary William E. McCall in front of his residence in Lomé, Togo

McCall took him to his dormitory quarters and introduced Jean-Marc to Sitobo Yosoufou, a young man from the Mossi tribe of Upper Volta, who was assigned to share a bunk bed with him. Yosoufou explained that his parents came from a Muslim tradition although they were nonbelievers and that they gave him the Muslim name Yosoufou, which means Joseph. He was grateful his name fitted his Christian faith.

Joseph and Jean-Marc became friends immediately. Jean-Marc soon shared his testimony with Joseph. He told Joseph how God had led him to the pastors' school to prepare to be a missionary to the people of Timbuktu. Joseph was as intrigued by Jean-Marc's story, as Jean-Marc was fascinated by Joseph's story.

Joseph came from a very poor family who lived in a small village a few kilometers from the city of Koudougou. His father, a farmer, eked out a living on the dry, parched land—barely enough to feed his family—and raised a few cattle. The cattle were so precious that often they ate more of the meager crops his father raised than the family did.

Baptist Theological School for West Africa, Lomé, Togo

His father had visited a nearby village and had seen how the people in that village had increased the productivity of their farms with the help of a Baptist missionary farmer named Ray Eitelman. Joseph's father, Sitobo Bawa, met Eitelman and asked him to visit his village and help the people there too. Eitelman came and showed them how to use yokes on a couple of the biggest Brahman steers owned by the village chief to pull metal plows to till the hard ground, instead of cultivating the soil by hand with a hoe. For several months Eitelman came to the village, helping the men in the village to plow the land and grow their crops. That year more grain grew than ever before in the village's history.

Joseph struck up a friendship with the missionary and every time Eitelman came to the village Joseph rushed out to talk with him. Even though his family was very poor, Joseph was one of the few young men of the village who had gone to elementary school and completed six years of study. He had learned to speak and to read French, and he often translated for Eitelman from French into Moré, the language of the Mossi people.

One day when Eitelman visited his village, Joseph asked him why he came so often to help the people and never asked anything in return. Eitelman told Joseph he came because he loved Jesus and Jesus loved the Mossi people. When Joseph asked, "Who is Jesus?" the missionary told him for the first time the story of God's love. He explained to Joseph that Jesus had died so that people could understand God's love.

The story touched Joseph's heart, and he told Eitelman he wanted to know God and to follow Jesus. With Joseph as his translator, Eitelman told the other people of the village about Jesus. Several of the men said they, too, wanted to follow Jesus. As a result, a small group began Bible study in the village. A Mossi Baptist leader named Bado Ambroise rode his bicycle to the village to lead the Bible study and preach to the people in the village.

Joseph became so excited about his newfound faith that he wanted to learn more. Eitelman encouraged him to enroll in a school nearby, where he could learn not only about the Bible,

Students in class of missionary Raymond Horne at the Baptist theological school in Togo

but also about a trade that would help him support himself and his family if later God led him to be a pastor. Joseph went to that school for two years, learning all he could from John Gray, the missionary director of the school. When he completed his study there, he and several other young men decided they wanted to study further and asked for permission to enroll in the Baptist School of Theology for West Africa. Joseph, however, was the only one who was able to come, and it strained his financial resources to the limit to do so.

Jean-Marc could tell that it also strained the school's educational requirements, for Joseph was not academically qualified for the pastors' school. Jean-Marc decided that the school's administration must have felt Joseph's motivation and intelligence could overcome his lack of education. Jean-Marc was glad that for some reason Joseph had been allowed to attend.

II

The next day McCall came by to see Jean-Marc and asked him if he would be interested in working as a *guardien* (night watchman) at the campus three nights each week. "It doesn't pay much, but maybe the job will help you take care of your living expenses that are not covered by your scholarship," he said.

Jean-Marc accepted willingly and agreed to start to work the next night. He was to guard the campus against robbers, patrol the grounds, and watch the gate from dark until dawn. Many of the other students worked as night watchmen also, rotating the responsibility around so that no one had too heavy a burden.

The first night on the job, Jean-Marc was ever so diligent. Not once did he go to sleep. He patrolled the campus and used his powerful flashlight whenever he heard something in the night. He was constantly on guard for snakes, especially the cobra and black mamba, but he saw none. Nothing happened all night long. It was the dullest job he had ever held.

The next day during his class on the life of Paul, Jean-Marc almost went to sleep. After class, Joseph asked him why he was so sleepy.

"Well, I didn't sleep any last night. Don't you remember? Last night was my night to work as the *guardien*."

Joseph laughed and quickly asked, "You mean you didn't sleep any at all?"

"No, I worked. I patrolled the grounds. I guarded the gate."

Joseph laughed even louder and slapped his leg. "You must never have worked as a *guardien* before. Don't you know that a *guardien* doesn't need to stay awake at night? All you need to do is get acquainted with the other *guardiens* in the neighborhood and form a pact with them. If you hear anything in the night, you must warn them, and if they hear anything, they will warn you. Then you find a good place near the gate and sleep on the ground."

When Jean-Marc asked if that wouldn't be cheating, Joseph answered: "All the big bosses know that this is the way *guardien* business works. They don't care. But just be careful that a robber doesn't break in, for then you will be in trouble!"

On Friday night Jean-Marc tried what Joseph suggested; sure enough, the system worked. The ground was hard, but the next day he wasn't nearly so tired. Joseph was right. Nothing happened at all. Only once did he awaken in the night when a dog started chasing one of the many rats who lived in the area.

It was an easy job and a good way to help pay his living expenses.

III

Jean-Marc, Agbalété Jacob, and four other passengers Jean-Marc and Jacob did not know bounced against each other, and sometimes against the roof of the bush taxi headed down the rough road from Adeti-Kopé, southeast toward Abobo, their destination. Jean-Marc was bursting with excitement not because it was his third trip to Abobo, but because this time he would be preaching for the first time in the Ewe language.

In the six months since he had arrived in Lomé Jean-Marc had learned to speak another language. Ewe, the principal language of most of the people in the Lomé area, was very similar to Fon, and Jean-Marc learned it quickly. The Ewe people and the Fon are close cousins, as African tribes go, and Jean-Marc saw many similarities between both the two languages and the customs.

This weekend was the third time he had visited Abobo with Jacob, the field evangelist for the Togo Baptist Association. Jacob was a former railroad engineer who had retired early and moved to Togo from eastern Ghana, where some Ewe live. He wanted to devote his full time to evangelistic work. His primary concern was teaching and training Ewe Christians how to witness effectively and how to start new churches.

Jacob and Jean-Marc were going to Abobo to start a new preaching point in a small nearby village near Lake Togo. It

Thatched-roof houses and granaries in Togo village

was a beautiful little village with about three hundred people living in the traditional mud huts with thatched roofs, clustered under a clump of trees. There was an established Baptist church in Abobo, and the new preaching point which Jacob and Jean-Marc hoped to start that weekend would be an additional evangelistic outreach led by the fairly new Christians of the church. Although the Abobo Baptists felt certain they could continue the work after it was started, they had asked for Jacob to come to help them get the preaching point going.

As they bounced along the bumpy road, Jacob explained to Jean-Marc his concept of starting new churches. In the past, the Togo Baptist Association had depended primarily on the Southern Baptist missionaries to help them start new work. In many cases the work had been built around a missionary, but this responsibility was now shared. Before, many of the people quit attending when the white man no longer came even though the preaching point was established and strong enough for the Togolese Baptists in the area to assume leadership. Jacob and three other Togolese Baptist leaders on the association's evangelism committee suggested, therefore, that missionaries train teams of Africans to start new work in the villages. "Then we can do away with those who just attend because 'the white man comes,' " Jacob explained. "Instead, we will only have those who come because they want to hear the word of God or because God has touched their lives and changed them. We may grow only a small church, but it will be a true church, and we won't have that falling away when the missionary leaves."

The idea made a lot of sense to Jean-Marc, and he was pleased to be one of the young men chosen to receive the training.

When they arrived in Abobo, Jacob and Jean-Marc walked with several local Baptist leaders to the small village on the shores of the lake. Jacob had lugged with him a portable gasoline generator, a 16mm movie projector, and a movie screen. The local leaders fussed over who would have the privilege of carrying the equipment, because it was a great status symbol to take the movie equipment into a village and show a film.

The sound track of the movie was in French. Because few of the people in such a small village spoke French, Jacob and Jean-Marc were prepared to translate the words of the movie into Ewe. They turned the volume of the sound track down low and shouted the translation in Ewe as loudly as they could. The result wasn't as good as an Ewe sound track, but seeing a movie was such a novel event that the people were pleased anyway.

After the movie, Jean-Marc preached on the story of Nicodemus, concluding with an evangelistic appeal based on John 3:16. When Jean-Marc stood before the crowd of villagers, he had never been happier. His words had a power that he never realized possible. The message flowed from his lips as smoothly as water cascading down a waterfall. Caught up in the thrill of preaching, Jean-Marc's spirit soared, and the people caught the spirit of his message, shouting words of encouragement. When Jean-Marc gave the invitation and Jacob led in the singing of a hymn to the beat of tribal drums, more than 12 people including the village chief came forward to say they wanted to accept Jesus. Before the crowd dispersed, Jacob asked all who had made decisions to return in the morning for a Bible study session.

Jean-Marc was too excited that night to sleep, even though the village chief had given him a private hut as a place of honor in appreciation for the sermon that had changed the chief's life. Jean-Marc knew that the chief's conversion was the key to the future success of the preaching point because now the entire village would look at the Baptist congregation with deep respect and honor. Jean-Marc prayed for hours, thanking God for the tremendous blessing of that day. He had never before experienced such joy.

He couldn't help remembering his first faltering experience at the Gran Yoff preaching point in Dakar, and how embarrassed he had been in front of Pastor Grossman. He wished the missionary could have been present tonight. Jean-Marc knew he would have been thrilled with the response. Even though all 12 Ewe people who made decisions might not follow through, that many decisions in one night equaled the total number of converts in 12 years among the Baptists in Senegal. Jean-Marc shook his head in amazement that God could use him in such a thrilling experience.

IV

As much as he loved preaching in the villages and helping Jacob start new churches, Jean-Marc had mixed emotions almost every time they went out for a weekend. He hated to miss a single service at the *Foyer Baptiste*. It was a congregation that met in the home of missionary Rex Holt, who had quickly become one of Jean-Marc's closest friends. Holt called the congregation the *foyer* because of the double meaning of the word in French. It meant not only "home" but also "hearth" or "fireside," and there was a warmth and love there that exceeded anything Jean-Marc had ever known.

Pastor Holt was as warm and compassionate as any missionary Jean-Marc knew. Not only that, Holt spoke French with a fluency rare among the American missionaries. He did student work at the University of Benin in Lomé, and was chairman of the Togo Baptist Mission that year.

Jean-Marc frequently taught one of the Bible classes at the *foyer*, but what he loved to do most was to sit in the class taught by Holt. The class was discussion-oriented, but Holt led the group into an understanding of the Scriptures that made Jean-Marc's head swim. Even though Jean-Marc might have read the passage many times before, Holt's insight into the Scriptures brought new meaning. Yet, his interpretation seemed to be so logical that Jean-Marc wondered why he had never thought of it before.

He often had the same experience in class at the Baptist School of Theology. Intellectually, however, his classes at school were not as much of a challenge to him as Pastor Holt's Bible study. Most of the people in Pastor Holt's classes were students at the University of Benin, or students at the *lycée* just down the street from the *foyer*. Academically, they were quite advanced.

Jean-Marc liked the theology courses taught by McCall and by Raymond Horne, but he wasn't as interested in the religious education courses. He liked the teacher, Phil Langley, but somehow Jean-Marc was not as interested in religious education as he was in theology, and especially in preaching.

On several occasions, Jean-Marc went into the villages with Don Glenn, the business manager of the mission, who had a deep love for work in the villages. Jean-Marc was amazed that a man whose training was in business and accounting could preach with such zeal and fervor. Glenn often would go out into one of the villages early on Sunday morning, lead an evangelistic service, and race back into Lomé in time for the 11:00 A.M. Sunday worship service at the Cocoteraie Baptist Church.

The pastor of the church was Clayton Bond, the tallest man Jean-Marc had ever seen. He towered over the African by almost two heads. He reminded Jean-Marc of a movie star he had seen once in a theater in Dakar that was showing American-made westerns with French subtitles. The movie star's name was John Wayne. In Pastor Bond's life, Jean-Marc saw that same quiet, towering strength that came through in the movie projection of Wayne. The Cocoteraie Baptist Church was located in a beautiful palm grove not far from the beach, and Jean-Marc loved to visit the church whenever he was not preaching in a village, or whenever Pastor Holt had to be gone from the *foyer*.

V

Because Jean-Marc seized every opportunity available to see different approaches to mission work and church development, he constantly stayed behind in writing letters. Even though Zukono could not read, Jean-Marc tried to write to him regularly, knowing that he would find someone who would read the letter to him.

Also he enjoyed writing to Diatta, Runyan, Cawthon, and especially Grossman to tell them briefly of his experiences and his love for preaching. But he had not written any letters for several weeks. The letter he had just written, though, might prove to be the most important he would ever write. He had set aside adequate time for it even though he had to miss a trip to a nearby village. This is what he wrote:

Dear Brice:
For several weeks, I've wanted to write to you but today is the first time I've had a chance. I've been busy,

not only with classes, but preparing sermons and preaching in the villages. Brice, I've come to love preaching more than I ever dreamed possible. The greatest thrill in my entire life was the night I preached in Ewe for the first time in a small village near Abobo. That night 12 adults, including the village chief, accepted Christ.

About three weeks ago, I was invited to give my testimony in the Boulevard Baptist Church here in Lomé, and it was an unforgettable experience. The church building is the most beautiful Baptist church I've ever seen anywhere. It even has a stained glass window above the balcony. Pastor Bond, who supervised construction of the building, told me the window was given to the church by a wealthy American widow from the state of Tennessee. It was assembled piece by piece here in Lomé. I've never heard such fervent singing in any African church, and the service lifted my soul almost to heaven itself.

But what is interesting about the Boulevard church, Brice, is that it is a Yoruba congregation. I was tremendously impressed by the spiritual commitment of the people there. The church does not have a full-time pastor, but three of the deacons do the preaching. One of them, Deacon Oke Isaac was in charge of the service the day I was asked to give my testimony. I was really impressed with his spiritual depth.

He and other members of the church gather at 5:30 every Monday and Thursday morning for a special prayer meeting, and they fast every Tuesday. On Friday nights, the key leaders who belong to the church's executive committee meet for another prayer meeting, and they have a special churchwide prayer meeting on Tuesday nights. They also have a Baptist Training Union, Sunday School, Women's Missionary Union, Girls' Auxiliary, and Royal Ambassadors.

Deacon Oke told me that the Yoruba here have made a definite attempt to reach the Togolese people, and at one time tried to hold services in French for the Togolese in addition to the services in Yoruba. The Yoruba churches cooperate in the Togo Baptist Association and give strong

Deacon Isaac Oke in front of his business establish-
ment in Lomé, Togo

financial support to the association. As in Abidjan, it was
the Yoruba who invited the Southern Baptists to send
missionaries to Togo. Pastor Bond was the first missionary to come here from Ghana as a result of the
Macedonian call from the Yoruba to come and help them
reach the Togolese.

I've made friends with several of the Yoruba young people, and they've invited me to come back on Sunday
night to their Baptist Training Union. Several Yoruba
young people made a deep impression on me, especially
a girl named Ruth.

It is late, and I must hurry to a meeting at the foyer.
Pleaes pray for me, Brice, as I continue to pray for you
and your ministry at Marcory church. Give my regards to
Pastor Darnell and the other missionaries I met in Abidjan. Please write when you have time, and pray for me
constantly. Proverbs 3:5-6.

Your brother in Christ,

Jean-Marc

A SECOND LOVE

I

Suprisingly, Jean-Marc was somewhat nervous as the young Yoruba man named Israel introduced him to the youth group at the Baptist Training Union at Boulevard Baptist Church. Jean-Marc didn't really know why he was nervous because he no longer felt scared or nervous even when he preached or gave his testimony.

Maybe it was the unknown. He had never before been to a BTU meeting, as the Yoruba called it. And tonight he was the leader! As best he could understand it, BTU was something like the "tea debates" he had attended back at *Ouagou Niayes* Baptist center in Dakar. Only in the case of BTU, the young people did not sit around and drink tea. They just talked about problems that affect the Christian life, and how they could be better Christians. There was also a strong emphasis on Bible study.

Israel had asked Jean-Marc to lead the discussion tonight on the challenge of Islam to Christianity and how Christians could be effective witnesses to Muslims. It was an interesting discussion. Jean-Marc told the Yoruba youth about his experiences in the predominantly Muslim society in Dakar and about the slow response to the gospel in Dakar compared to the response in Togo. He told them about the role of the marabouts, the Islamic priests who control much of the Islamic culture in Dakar, and the formal ritualism. He told them about Pierre's search for meaning in life and his discovery of what he was looking for in Jesus.

The Yoruba youth asked perceptive questions, especially a young woman named Ruth, who had the most beautiful eyes Jean-Marc had ever seen. They seemed like big brown islands floating on huge white clouds. There was a softness in those eyes that made Jean-Marc's heart melt every time he looked into them.

After the program, Ruth shyly walked up to Jean-Marc along with a group of young people and asked him several questions. Israel invited Jean-Marc to go with a group of the young people afterwards to a fellowship at the home of one of the members, and Jean-Marc was delighted to accept. When he found himself at Ruth's house, Jean-Marc's heart skipped a beat.

At the fellowship that night, Jean-Marc met Ruth's father, Adejumo Samuel, and her mother, Ibiyemi. They called Ruth *"Ayoka,"* one who causes joy all around. Jean-Marc thought the name was perfect for Ruth!

He liked Samuel and Samuel seemed to like Jean-Marc. He was very complimentary of Jean-Marc's testimony, telling him how much it meant to him. Samuel, like most Yoruba, was a trader. He bought and sold expensive cloth that was re-sold in the markets not only in Lomé but also in Abidjan, Dakar, and Cotonou.

Jean-Marc also struck up a friendship with Israel, the leader of the BTU group, and they talked about significant questions of the faith that had troubled each of them. Israel seemed genuinely impressed with Jean-Marc's knowledge of the Bible and his ability to communicate. Even though the Yoruba worship services are conducted in the Yoruba language, most of the BTU sessions were in French, which the young people spoke even more fluently than Yoruba. It was the language they used in *collège* (elementary school) and *lycée,* and it was the language of ideas and concepts. Jean-Marc liked the Yoruba. He was anxious to write Brice more about the Yoruba in Togo.

While he and Israel talked, Ruth often slipped into the small circle of young people and listened quietly. She didn't say much, but Jean-Marc hoped he was making a good impression on her. He was smitten by her charm and beauty.

Israel told Jean-Marc that in three weeks the group would be discussing the problem that occurs among Christian groups that try to mix animism and Christianity to form an unusual form of African "Christianity." When Israel realized that Jean-Marc had some insight on the subject, he asked him to come back to lead the discussion. Jean-Marc accepted immediately.

Later, he wondered what in the world he would say. Actually he had never prepared a paper or a talk on syncretism, which is the word used for the practice of combining different religious beliefs and practices. He had heard Pastor Holt discuss the subject, but besides that, he knew only what he had observed. He knew he would really have to prepare well for the discussion. Jean-Marc didn't want to look bad to the girl with the most haunting eyes he had ever seen.

II

Rex Holt was extremely helpful when Jean-Marc asked him to explain syncretism. In West African religious practice, he explained, syncretism means to worship Christ and the tribal gods of animism at the same time. He said that several African churches actually mixed ancestor worship and fetishism with Christianity in a deliberate way. One is called the Christian Celeste church, and another is the Cherubim and Seraphim Independent Church.

"Although most priests will deny it, syncretism has crept into the Catholic churches in West Africa also," Holt added. "The use of the crucifix and statues of Mary, Jesus, and the saints in Catholic rituals may make some African Catholics less likely to oppose the use of additional sacred objects like fetishes. They may not be used in actual worship at the church, but many Catholics that come from a background of fetish worship continue to use fetishes in their worship practices at home," he said.

Jean-Marc talked about the problems of syncretism not only with Holt, but also with missionaries McCall and Horne. Some of the best help he received, however, came not on the theory of syncretism, but on its practice. He talked to his friend and co-worker Jacob and to Akakpo Vizah Millissor, a student at the pastors' school whose father was a fetish priest among the Ewe.

Vizah took Jean-Marc to meet his father, and they talked at length about fetishism. Vizah also took him to the fetish market in the Bé section of Lomé, just across the lagoon from the school. Jean-Marc was amazed at the number of skulls, bones, skins, dried whole frogs, crocodiles and snakes, herbs, and pottery items that were for sale in the fetish market. He had seen fetish markets, but nothing like this. He was overcome by the pervasive power of fear that he could feel in the atmosphere. Many of the people who came to the market to buy objects prescribed by the fetish priest looked frightened. They sincerely believed in the magic of the fetish.

As they walked back toward the lagoon, Vizah took Jean-Marc by the sacred forest of Bé, the home of a large number of Ewe fetish priests. They didn't enter the forest because Vizah said the power of evil seemed to lurk there.

Jean-Marc walked away from the market and sacred forest convinced that satanic power was behind fetishism. As they walked along the dusty road, Vizah shared his personal testimony with Jean-Marc. Vizah's father wanted him to become a fetish priest because he was the eldest son. When Vizah rejected fetishism for Christianity, his father even suggested that if he felt God wanted him to be a Christian pastor, he should be a Catholic priest, not a Baptist who rejected fetishism totally.

As they talked, Jean-Marc realized that Vizah should be the person invited to lead the session on syncretism at the Boulevard Baptist Church, but he did not make the suggestion either to Israel or Vizah. Jean-Marc wanted an opportunity to make a good impression on Ruth.

When the time came, Jean-Marc felt good about his preparation. He began his presentation by defining syncretism and dealing first with the theoretical aspects. But he spent most of his time on Vizah's story.

"Vizah always believed God had a special purpose for his life because of an experience he had as a very young boy. He fell into the cookfire, burning his arms and back severely. He almost died the next morning, but by night he seemed to recover miraculously. Vizah believes that Satan knew God had a special purpose for his life and was trying to kill Vizah to prevent him from fulfilling God's plan.

"When he was a schoolboy, Vizah began going to a Catholic church where the people mixed Christianity with fetishism. He did not learn that Jesus was the only way really to know God.

"Shortly after Vizah and his family moved to the city of Lomé, he was walking down the street and met a white man passing out Christian tracts. The man was Raymond Horne, professor at the Baptist School of Theology. When Horne found out Vizah's father was a fetish priest, he made a special effort to lead Vizah to accept Jesus as Savior. Vizah did accept Christ, but his father was so angry he would no longer pay Vizah's educational costs. That meant Vizah could no longer go to school. His younger brother, Toho, who also accepted Christ the same day, didn't receive his father's wrath because he wasn't the oldest son.

"For a month, Vizah had studied how to become a fetish priest with his father. He had learned some of the secrets of fetishism and was convinced that fetishism was demonic. Even his father admitted fetish objects themselves have no power, but that the power was in the secret words said by the fetish priest when he casts a spell using the fetish.

"The fetish priest also claims to use his power to put a curse on someone, to cause the roof of a house to cave in, or to kill someone. Vizah's father at one time became so angry with Vizah after he rejected fetishism that he actually put a curse on his own son. Vizah's brother told him he was supposed to be dead in three days. On the night of the third day, a heavy rock crashed through the roof of his house and hit the floor just a few feet from where Vizah was sleeping. Vizah was very afraid until he took his Bible and read Psalm 23.

"The next day Vizah's father came into his room and asked why there was a hole in the ceiling. Vizah replied that a stone had fallen through his roof but God had protected him from evil.

"In spite of Vizah's brother's plea to their father to leave Vizah alone, Vizah's father keeps placing fetishes to keep

Vizah from going to church. Of course, Vizah just kicks them aside and goes on."

Jean-Marc's concluding statement condemned the practice of mixing any old beliefs with Christian doctrine. "I am convinced that Christians like Vizah who totally reject fetishism are right because fetishism is evil. To mix it with Christianity is like trying to mix oil with water. The two are simply not compatible."

Citing several Scripture passages warning against demonic powers and admonishing followers of Christ to reject the evil ways of the world, he exhorted Yoruba youth to examine their own lives to see if there were ways they might be open to the power of Satan—ways that they might try to mix their Christian faith with the ways of the world.

The young people gave Jean-Marc an overwhelming response. But what melted his heart was Ruth's response. Looking up at him with those beautiful eyes, she said. "Oh, Jean-Marc. You were just terrific!"

Jean-Marc thought he was in heaven itself.

III

At times, Jean-Marc felt torn between two loves—his love for preaching and his newfound love for Ruth. Never before had he felt this way about anyone. He wanted to be with her every possible moment.

Even when he was studying and going to classes, he was constantly thinking about Ruth. On his way to the villages to preach, at times he felt his mind wandering, always back to those beautiful eyes. Only when he stood before a village congregation to preach, was he able to put her from his mind. Proclaiming the good news of Jesus Christ was his first commitment.

Whenever Jean-Marc wasn't going to class, studying for an exam, preaching in the villages, or working as the night watchman at school, he spent as much time as possible with Ruth. They went several times to *Foyer Baptiste* together, and Ruth immediately liked Rex Holt and the young people there. The couple took walks together, sharing on a level that reminded Jean-Marc of his deep friendship with Pierre. But this was different. He was in love. And so was Ruth.

It soon became obvious to Ruth's parents that their daughter had found a special suitor. Though Ruth was still a student in the *lycée*, she was of marriageable age. But after the family's move to Lomé from a village in Nigeria seven years before, the young man her family had selected as her intended husband had been killed when a car crashed into his bicycle. Since then, the family had found no suitable candidate for marriage to Ruth.

Jean-Marc was unaware that their relationship caused a disagreement in Ruth's family. Ruth's father, Samuel, liked Jean-Marc immediately after meeting him the night he gave his testimony at the Yoruba church. He considered Jean-Marc a worthy suitor for his daughter even though he was not Yoruba. Of course, he wanted his daughter to marry in their tribe, but he saw in Jean-Marc strong qualities that he felt would make him a good husband and father. He approved of Jean-Marc without reservation.

Ruth's mother, Ibiyemi, however, was highly reluctant to give her approval of Jean-Marc. She knew nothing of Jean-Marc's family and had no way of knowing whether his family was tainted with hereditary diseases. Even though her family was Christian, she still felt strongly that the Yoruba marriage customs and traditions should be observed. Besides, she argued, it was too early yet even to think of marriage. If some time in the future their relationship developed to the point that Jean-Marc's family asked for Ruth's hand in marriage, she might consider it; but only after the traditional Yoruba investigation of Jean-Marc's family, and only after the observance of the Yoruba custom of *isihun*, which grants formal consent for the betrothal, engagement, and marriage. She made her feelings very clear. If Jean-Marc wanted to marry Ruth, a lot of questions would have to be answered first.

CRISIS IN KOUDOUGOU

I

 The week of final exams at the end of his first year at the Baptist School of Theology for West Africa was almost over. Jean-Marc cheerfully walked into his dormitory room, only to find his bunk-mate, Joseph, so upset that he was almost in tears.

Joseph had just received a cable from his father in Koudougou. It told of the drought that had hit Upper Volta so hard there was famine and widespread disease. Death and starvation were rampant. Joseph's sister had died of some unknown disease, and his mother was gravely ill. Joseph's father asked his son to return to Koudougou immediately.

"What shall I do, Jean-Marc?" Joseph moaned. "I still have two more finals to take, and they are in my hardest subjects. If I stay to take the tests, I'm afraid I will be so upset that I will flunk the exams. But if I leave before the tests, I will lose all that I have worked so hard to achieve this year."

It was a real dilemma, and Jean-Marc didn't know what to advise. But he knew Joseph needed some guidance. "I'll go with you if you want me to, but first, let's take the cable to Pastor McCall and explain the situation. He will know what to do," Jean-Marc reassured him.

The seminary president was very understanding when Joseph and Jean-Marc told him of the problem. He told Joseph that his family deserved the highest priority. Then he asked, "What exams have you not taken? When are they scheduled?"

The first test, in New Testament theology, was the next morning, a Thursday, and the final test was in homiletics (preaching) on Thursday afternoon. McCall suggested that since taking his exams would delay his trip only one day, Joseph should go ahead and take them and do the best he could.

The next day Joseph took both exams and finished discouraged over the results and absolutely exhausted emotionally and physically. But he was glad to have no unfinished business hanging over him as he prepared for the long journey home.

When he returned to his room, Joseph lay on his bunk and wept under the emotional strain of the day. He was grateful Jean-Marc had offered to go with him to Koudougou. He didn't think he could make the trip alone.

When Jean-Marc came to their room that evening, Joseph offered to pay Jean-Marc's bus fare to Koudougou. As poor as he and his father were, Joseph wanted to show his gratitude for Jean-Marc's offer to go home with him.

Jean-Marc was torn apart by two desires. He wanted to help his friend, and he had really meant his offer to go with Joseph; yet, he didn't want to be away from Ruth for so long. But when he saw Joseph almost coming apart emotionally, Jean-Marc's heart went out to his brother in Christ. "Before we leave," he said, "I want to talk to Ruth." He didn't tell Joseph that Ruth knew nothing about his family's problems.

When Jean-Marc arrived at Ruth's house, her father had just come home. Jean-Marc explained Joseph's problem to him.

"I am glad you are going with him," Samuel said. "If your brother is in need and if you can help him, that is what you should do. I feel certain Ruth will agree, but I don't think that Joseph or his father should pay your bus fare in the light of the circumstances. Let me make a proposal to you. Today, God richly blessed me. I was able to sell an entire year's supply of material to a new department store that is being built in Abidjan. I want to use some of the money that God has given me today to help you and Joseph travel to Koudougou. Whatever the bus tickets to Koudougou cost, I will pay for them."

Jean-Marc was thrilled with the offer, even though he was reluctant to accept. But Samuel insisted that God had laid it on his heart to offer the bus fare to the young men.

When Ruth came into the room, her beautiful eyes accented by a colorful head piece she had wrapped around her freshly shampooed hair, Jean-Marc told her about Joseph's cable from his father. At first, her eyes reflected distress at the thought of Jean-Marc's being gone for three weeks. But then concern and compassion replaced her disappointment as she realized that Jean-Marc would be able to minister to the needs of Joseph and his family in a way that perhaps no other person could. She encouraged him to go.

Jean-Marc returned to his room with the money in his pocket for the two tickets, rejoicing that God supplies every need of those who seek to follow his will. When he told Joseph what Ruth and her father had said, Joseph fell on his knees in thanksgiving to God for Samuel's gift.

Joseph sent a cable to his father saying they would arrive at 6:00 p.m. on Saturday. Then, exhausted from the strain of the day, both young men slept well that night. Early the next morning they were ready to catch the *mille kilos* bus (thousand kilos—a 22-passenger bus used between towns and villages throughout West Africa) north to Upper Volta.

II

It took two days of hard travel for them to arrive in Koudougou. They went by *mille kilos* bus from Lomé north to Atakpamé, and then on to Sokodé, about halfway up the long, 100-kilometer-wide country of Togo. After crossing the Toto Mountains, they headed north to Dapango, about 15 kilometers from the Upper Volta border. On the same highway, they headed due north past Tenkoudougou, and then west to Ouagadougou, the capital city of Upper Volta. Although he had heard the names of the cities all his life, Jean-Marc was intrigued with the poetic sound of the names —Koudougou, Ouagadougou, and Tenkoudougou. From the capital city of Ouagadougou, they took a train west to Koudougou.

Throughout the trip to Upper Volta, Jean-Marc was overwhelmed by what he had seen. The land was parched and barren. Because the country's only rainy season, which

Missionary Norman Coad and evangelist Kabore
François distributing grain and food in Upper Volta

usually starts in May, was late, the land was suffering from the worst drought since the terrible famine of 1970-71. Water holes where the cattle normally were able to get enough water to stay alive were dried and cracked with clay-baked mud. It was not uncommon to see a dead cow, its bones protruding from its stiff hide, lying in the middle of the road. Once the bus driver had to stop to pull a carcass off the highway.

As devastated as the countryside was, the people looked worse. Everywhere he looked, Jean-Marc saw the hideous results of malnutrition and starvation. Young children with bloated bellies begged in the streets of Ouagadougou for food and money. Jean-Marc saw old men and women whose emaciated bodies were so thin and weak they did not have enough strength to stand and beg. They literally lay on the roadsides, holding outstretched cups as they begged for alms.

Malnutrition is a way of life for many of the peope in West Africa, and Jean-Marc had seen its effects since early childhood. But never had he seen anything like this before. With his forehead furrowed with wrinkles of compassion, Jean-Marc looked out the bus and train windows, his vision clouded by tears mixed with dust. Dust was everywhere. Never had he seen so much dust, even in Dakar. Most of all, never had he experienced such suffering among the people.

Joseph feared the worst when he and Jean-Marc stepped off the crowded train and greeted his father. He was right. His mother was dead. She had been so weak from lack of proper nourishment that she had died during her sleep. The family had scheduled the funeral for the next morning, hoping Joseph would arrive in time.

Joseph did not seem to suffer as much grief over his mother's death as Jean-Marc had expected. Most of the trip he had simply sat in the seat by the window and stared out into space. It was as if he knew what would be awaiting him when he arrived in Koudougou. By the time they arrived, Joseph seemed numb. He did not even weep when his father said his mother was dead. After the funeral, Jean-Marc wanted to talk to Joseph about returning to Lomé, but he could tell he needed to wait a while longer. The next day when Jean-Marc mentioned it, Joseph pleaded with him to stay. "Don't go back yet. Stay a few more days. I want you to meet Pastor Eitelman and to visit the Rural Training Center, where I went to school. But I need to be at home for another day or two before I leave to go into Koudougou to take you to meet Pastor Eitelman and Pastor Gray."

So Jean-Marc stayed in the small village outside Koudougou, trying to comfort his friend and the family. At times he was bored, but he loved and respected his friend too much to show it.

Two days later, Joseph and Jean-Marc traveled to Koudougou to meet Eitelman. Jean-Marc was surprised to see that the pastor whom Joseph loved so much walked with a limp. Joseph had not mentioned Eitelman was crippled from polio. When asked about Eitelman later, Joseph responded, "Well, I've never even thought of him as a cripple."

Eitelman showed Jean-Marc how he had tried to help the people of the villages by digging wells. "There is nothing as precious in this country as water," he explained. "We've helped dig wells in about 15 villages near Koudougou; and in every village where we have been able to dig a well and find water, we've also been able to start a church."

Eitelman also told him about training the people in the villages to use a bullock or steer with a yoke to do the plowing. Before, they used a hand-held hoe. When people change from human power to animal power in plowing, they can greatly increase the productivity of their fields.

"But without water, nothing will grow, and Upper Volta is without water in a way that people living here who are my age have experienced only once before," Eitelman said.

When Jean-Marc visited the Rural Training Center, where Joseph had gone to school, he was amazed by some of the ingenious ideas that John Gray had brought to the village people. One of the most amazing things was a hand-powered washing machine. Made of wood with a water-tight metal sink inside, the washing machine featured a hand lever that went up and down, causing two rubber-covered pistons to agitate the water and clothes up and down. Gray explained that the wooden washing machine costs about 20 dollars to make, but it saves enough water so that all the clothes in an entire village can be washed with the amount of water one or two families would normally use.

Another ingenious invention was a cookstove that cut by two-thirds the amount of firewood needed. Gray explained

Missionary John Gray watching woman at stove he invented

that every tree cut in this area of Upper Volta intensifies the ecological imbalance and hastens the kind of drought that the country is now experiencing. One reason so many trees are cut is that most women cook with three pots, each one heated by a separate fire. Each pot sits on top of three rocks, with the wood burning beside the stones beneath the pots. Gray designed a unique mud-clay cookstove which uses only one wood fire to heat three pots. One pot sits on top of an open fire, but all the heat and smoke from that fire is sucked through a chimney that leads to a second pot, and on to the third pot before the heat and smoke is pulled by the draft out the tall chimney. Thus, he explained, the wood for only one fire heats three pots. The stove is fairly easy to make with materials that are readily available in any village for a minimum cost.

Although classes at the Rural Training Center were not in session at the time, Gray and Joseph showed Jean-Marc the classrooms where Bible studies are taught and the big work-room where students learn a trade. Gray explained that most churches in Upper Volta have so little money they cannot afford to pay their pastors a living wage. Almost all pastors must support themselves by working in some trade. Gray said most of them are farmers, but the Rural Training School has taught other trades to many. It has taught them how to build and sell guitars, how to make bronze castings of art objects for sale to tourists, and how to do leather work and carpentry.

Jean-Marc was fascinated by all that he learned and over-whelmed by the needs of the people. He was astounded to hear that 90 percent of the people in Upper Volta are illiterate. But he was encouraged when he learned that Monica Keathley, a Southern Baptist missionary in Ouagadougou, was devoting her full-time efforts to literacy missions work and using the Bible to teach people to read.

Expressing his concern for the people suffering from the drought, Jean-Marc asked Gray if there was anything he could do personally to help while he was in the country.

Gray thought for a moment and then offered a suggestion.

Woman pulling bucket of water from well that was part of the agricultural project at Koudougou, Upper Volta

"Yes, I think there is something you can do right now. When you travel back to Togo, you will pass through Tenkoudougou, where Southern Baptist relief worker Norman Coad and agricultural missionary Larry Cox are involved in the biggest world hunger and disaster relief project Southern Baptists have ever undertaken. It is a massive relief project to provide water for people of 10 villages near Tenkoudougou. Right now, Norman needs volunteers who will help dig wells in several of the villages, and I'm sure he would be delighted if you stopped there for a week or two to help on the project."

Jean-Marc was excited by the idea. He knew that Ruth and the people in Lome were not expecting him to return for another two weeks, and he felt he could probably do more to help the people of Upper Volta by working as a volunteer in the well-digging project than in any other way.

Joseph, naturally, did not want Jean-Marc to leave so soon. But when he realized that what Jean-Marc would be doing might prevent the kind of malnutrition in Tenkoudougou that killed his own mother and sister in Koudougou, he willingly sent Jean-Marc on the mission.

For 10 days Jean-Marc worked in the Tenkoudougou project, doing the most backbreaking labor of his life. Every night he was bone-tired. But every night he went to sleep knowing what he was doing might help the people have enough water to grow enough food to keep them from malnutrition and starvation.

Jean-Marc immediately liked Norman Coad. He saw in Coad compassion for people that expressed itself in the most practical way possible. Yet, Coad never had any hesitancy in telling people about the living water that Jesus Christ provides, and he loved to tell the story of the Samaritan woman at the well.

When the 10 days were up, Jean-Marc was sorry in some ways to leave. Never had he found such personal satisfaction in hard manual labor. Never had he felt that he was doing something specific that might prevent death and starvation and disease. He had come to love the Mossi people in a way he had not known before. He realized meeting people's physical needs in the name of Christ was a vital ministry.

But his first love and his second love still beckoned him back to Lomé.

III

The trip from Tenkoudougou back to Lomé seemed to Jean-Marc twice as long as the trip from Lomé to Koudougou, even though it was 280 kilometers shorter. Jean-Marc wanted to get back to Lomé and Ruth as soon as possible. As he traveled in the *mille kilos* bus across the Upper Volta border back into Togo, his thoughts were dominated by those beautiful brown eyes, beckoning him back to Lomé.

More than anything else right now, Jean-Marc wanted to ask Ruth to be his wife. It did not matter to him that she was Yoruba and he was Fon. He felt certain that his father would not approve of his marrying anyone but a Fon girl; but the fact that Ruth was not Fon did not matter nearly so much to Jean-Marc as the fact that she was a Christian.

He realized, however, that before he could marry Ruth, he had hurdles to overcome. The first was to obtain her parents' permission, and he did not know how they might feel about her marrying someone who was not Yoruba. The second was to obtain his father's blessing. He knew that would be difficult. As for getting Ruth to agree to be his wife, Jean-Marc was more hopeful. They had talked secretly of the possibility of marriage, but only in vague and general terms. Jean-Marc felt sure that Ruth loved him as much as he loved her, although neither had spoken those words.

As the bus bounced over the bumpy road, Jean-Marc thought of nothing but his goal of marriage to Ruth. Suddenly an idea flashed in his mind. His father had often talked of the possibility of returning to his native village of Gomé, Benin, to visit his brother and other members of his family. Jean-Marc decided to write Zukono a letter, inviting him to come to Lomé and then travel with Jean-Marc back to Gomé for a visit. Jean-Marc didn't know whether Zukono would be willing to leave his work for the two months that such a trip

would probably require, but he prayed the prospect of returning home would convince him.

Jean-Marc planned to introduce Zukono to Ruth's parents
during his stay in Lomé. He realized it was risky. Both
parents might dislike each other and oppose the marriage
even more as a result. Somehow, though, he felt this was the
best way to get the blessings of the two families for the
betrothal and marriage.

In his mind, he began to draft a letter to his father. Then he
started planning the words with which he would ask Ruth to
be his wife. If she said yes, and Jean-Marc was certain that
she would, they could plan together the best way to obtain
their parents' approval.

One thing was certain. He would do anything possible and
right to be able to claim Ruth as his bride.

LOVE FINDS A WAY

I

 The *mille kilos* bus pulled into Lomé at 5:16
P.M. on Sunday, two weeks and two days
after Jean-Marc and Joseph had left the city.
Jean-Marc rushed from the *gare* (bus station), where the bus unloaded, to his room
on the campus. As quickly as possible he washed and
changed clothes, then took the bus west on the *Boulevard
Circulaire* to the Boulevard Baptist Church. He rushed to get
there before BTU started because he wanted to see Ruth's
face when she saw him earlier than she expected.

He had written to her every other day, giving her a detailed account of his experience, but he suspected most of the letters had not yet arrived in Lomé.

When Jean-Marc's bus stopped near the church, nobody was there. He waited under the shade of a small tree with branches hanging over a narrow alley between the church and a wall separating the church property from an apartment compound next door. It was hot, but Jean-Marc did not notice. All he thought about was seeing Ruth.

As Ruth stepped off the bus and saw Jean-Marc waiting, her eyes brightened even more than they usually did when she saw Jean-Marc. She rushed to his side and almost embraced him publicly, restraining herself at the last minute. She and Jean-Marc knew it would not be appropriate to display their affection publicly on the sidewalk, especially in front of the church. They walked together into the alleyway beside the church, wanting so much to embrace.

Ruth had received only two letters, the first telling about the trip to Koudougou and the death of Joseph's mother, and the second telling about Jean-Marc's visit with Pastor Gray and Pastor Eitelman. In the second letter, Jean-Marc had mentioned the possibility that he might stop in Tenkoudougou to work in the hunger relief project, but that was all she had heard.

Jean-Marc had so many things to tell Ruth that he didn't know where to start. One all-consuming question, however, burned like a West African brushfire in his heart. He wanted to blurt out the question immediately but knew he must wait for the right moment.

"I must talk with you," he whispered as they walked into the meeting room. "May I walk home with you tonight?"

Her beautiful eyes shining, she nodded quietly as they sat down together. Later, neither could remember what the program was that night. Their minds were on one thing—each other!

Jean-Marc and Ruth started hand in hand down the *Boulevard Circulaire* toward Ruth's home in the *Olympio Nétime* section of the city about four kilometers east of the church. At first they chatted about routine matters—the lack of rain, the health of Ruth's family, the long trip, how Joseph was doing. Then Ruth asked Jean-Marc what the trip that distance by bus was like.

Jean-Marc responded indirectly to her question, using her question as an opening for him to say what he had been wanting to say for two days. "It was a terribly long, lonely trip," he responded. "At times on the bus, I was bored, but I had a lot of time to think." Stopping on the sidewalk beneath a small tree, Jean-Marc turned to face Ruth and continued. "I thought about you constantly, Ruth. I missed you so terribly much. Being away from you made me realize how much I love you. I want to spend the rest of my life with you by my side. More than anything else, I want you to be my wife. May I talk to your father and ask his permission for you to be my wife?"

"Oh, yes, Jean-Marc," she answered. "I feel the same way. These last two weeks have been torture for me. I've missed you more than words can say. I love you very, very much."

Their eyes met. Then their lips met, and their separate heartbeats seemed to merge into one.

So enthralled in their love were they that they were oblivious of anything else. Suddenly, it dawned on Ruth that they were embracing on the sidewalk of a busy boulevard. She pulled away, and the two lovers proceeded down the street.

As they walked along, they discussed the best way to approach her parents. Jean-Marc reminded her he did not know the customs for asking permission to marry a Yoruba girl. Ruth responded that she thought her father would grant his permission. He liked Jean-Marc and was more "modern" and less bound by the traditional Yoruba customs than her mother. "Because mother is so traditional and is very concerned about the old tribal customs, she probably has reservations about you and your family," Ruth said.

She explained that if she were living back in her hometown of Iwo, near Ibadan, Nigeria, Jean-Marc would ask an uncle to go to her father's oldest brother to request her hand in marriage. The uncles would handle all the negotiations between the two families concerning the arrangements for the formal engagement and marriage. "But since neither your uncle nor my uncle lives in Lomé, I would suggest that you talk to Deacon Oke at the church and see what he advises," Ruth said.

Jean-Marc shared with Ruth his idea of writing a letter to his father inviting him to come to Lomé for a visit so he could meet Ruth and her family. Of course, he pointed out, his father would think the purpose of the visit was to travel together back to his father's hometown in Gomé, not far from Abomey, Benin.

Ruth liked the idea. She thought her mother might have fewer reservation about the marriage if she could meet Jean-Marc's father and find out more about his family background.

When they parted that night, Jean-Marc walked to the bus and back to his room so blissfully that he hardly knew when his feet touched the ground. It was as if he were walking on clouds with his face peeking into heaven itself.

II

It took 18 long days for Jean-Marc to get a response from his letter to his father. When the letter came, Jean-Marc's hands trembled as he opened it.

It was from Diatta, his friend at the *Centre Baptiste* in Dakar. Knowing his father could not read or write, Jean-Marc had written to Diatta, explaining his secret plan and enclosing an envelope personally addressed to Zukono. Stressing why it was so important for Zukono to come to Lomé to meet Ruth's father, Jean-Marc asked Diatta to deliver the letter to his father personally, to read the letter to him, and to write back immediately with Zukono's response.

There was a nervous rumble in Jean-Marc's stomach as he read Diatta's letter:

Dear Jean-Marc:
I was pleased to learn you have found a wonderful Christian girl to be your wife. I am praying that she is, in-

deed, the one woman in the world God has chosen to be your mate.

As you requested, I took your letter to your father and read it to him; but I did not mention to him anything about your desire to be married. At first, I couldn't tell how he liked the idea of coming to visit you. But as we talked, he began to show great interest in your invitation. He told me he had always wanted to return to Gomé and had feared for several years that his older brother might die before he could see him again. He told me that if he ever was to make a trip home to Benin, now was perhaps the best time of his life. He dictated to me the following letter, which I attach.

> *Your brother in Christ,*
> *Diatta*

Jean-Marc's hand trembled even more as he opened the second envelope and read the note from his father:

My dear son Amasou:
I have thought a great deal about your invitation to come to Lomé and travel with you to Gomé, and I would like to do this. I am not sure exactly when I can leave Dakar because there are many arrangements to be made. I have been thinking about quitting my job at the nail factory, and maybe even moving back to Gomé. I have not been happy since you left Dakar. Narie is worse than ever before, and I have thought about divorcing her. If it were not for the children, I would leave her, quit my job, and move back to Dahomey. Your letter came at exactly the right time, for it has given me hope and encouragement for the future. Whatever I decide to do about my relationship with Narie, I have definitely decided to come to Lomé and travel with you to Gomé. I will send you a cable once I know when I will leave Dakar and when I expect to arrive in Lomé.

> *Your loving father,*
> *Zukono*

III

After a hard day's work, Jean-Marc was tired, but he wanted to make one more important stop on the way home. Shortly after he had returned from the trip to Koudougou, he had found a job as a cook's helper at the restaurant in the *Hotel Rama Palais,* located on the *Boulevard de la République,* which leads along the coastline to the Ghana border. Before meals, Jean-Marc chopped and prepared the vegetables, and after meals, he washed dishes. Today he had worked both breakfast and lunch shifts. He knew he would have to quit his job when his father arrived in Lomé, but he wanted to work as long as possible to earn money for next year's school expenses. Most important of all, he wanted to earn money for the dowry necessary for marriage to Ruth.

That, in part, was the purpose of his visit with Deacon Oke. At his sewing supply shop Deacon Oke sold buttons, needles, thread, and sewing machine parts. Although the shop was small, it was distinctive. On the wall above the door leading to the shop, Deacon Oke had painted a sign that said "Amen," his own praise to God for answering the prayers he voiced so frequently. Smiling broadly when he saw Jean-Marc, Deacon Oke invited him inside to talk.

Inside the shop, Jean-Marc greeted Deacon Oke and chatted graciously for several minutes. He asked about his family, his business, the church, and about anything else that came to mind. Deacon Oke, in turn, asked about Jean-Marc's trip to Upper Volta, his new job at the restaurant, his plans for the future at the pastors' school, his activities at the *Foyer Baptiste,* and his visits to the BTU.

Finally, after an appropriate time of discussion about unrelated matters, Jean-Marc came to the point of his visit. "Deacon Oke, I have a problem that I need to discuss with you. I need your advice. Would it be possible for me to talk privately with you?"

Deacon Oke had already guessed why Jean-Marc had come, but he gave no indication. "Of course, Jean-Marc," he replied. "I will be happy to talk to you and help you in any way that I can. It is almost time for me to close my shop. Now is a good time for me to talk with you unless you have something else you need to do."

Jean-Marc gratefully accepted Deacon Oke's offer and at Oke's suggestion rode with him on his motor scooter to the nearby *Place de l'Indépendance.* There they sat under the cool shade of a big mango tree sipping cold drinks that Deacon Oke bought for them.

They sat quietly for a few moments, and then Deacon Oke spoke. "Tell me about this problem, and how I can advise you."

Jean-Marc told him he wanted Ruth to be his wife. He also explained the plans to get Zukono's permission and that of Jean-Marc's uncle in Benin. "I know the customs of the Fon regarding marriage, but I don't know the customs of the Yoruba, and I need your advice on how my family should approach her family to ask for her hand in marriage," Jean-Marc said.

Deacon Oke paused for a moment before answering and then responded. "It will not be easy to arrange. Marriage for the Yoruba as well as for the Fon is not just between two individuals. It is between two families.

"As you know, Adejumo Samuel comes from the village of Iwo in Nigeria. It will be necessary to get permission from his oldest brother, who lives there. Fortunately, I know very well the pastor of the Iwo Baptist Church, where the family is very active, and I may be able to help. But it will take time. They may not like the idea of Ruth marrying someone from the Fon tribe, but I suspect the marriage customs of the Fon are quite similar to those of the Yoruba. Tell me about the Fon customs, and I will tell you how the Yoruba customs differ from those of your own people."

<h2 style="text-align:center">IV</h2>

"Since I was a boy," began Jean-Marc, "my father has been careful to teach me the traditions of the Fon, especially the customs regarding engagement and marriage. He has always wanted me to marry a Fon girl because I am his only

Fon son. Because there were no Fon girls in Dakar, my father had always hoped that someday we would return to Benin to arrange my marriage to a Fon girl. We both have lived in the city long enough for many of the old tribal ways to become unimportant to me, but not to my father. To me, it is far more important to marry a fine Christian girl who will support me as a pastor than it is to marry a Fon. But my father still follows tribal ways. That's why I need your advice."

Nodding in agreement, Deacon Oke pursued his earlier question. "If Ruth were from the Fon tribe, what customs and procedures would you follow in asking for her hand in marriage and in getting the approval of both families?"

"Well, if I remember the customs correctly," replied Jean-Marc, "I would make my choice known to my uncle, who is the head of our family as the oldest living male. My uncle would then talk to the other influential members of our family to see if they think Ruth's family is acceptable. Then he would talk to one of my aunts, who is known as the *tanino* or marriage arranger. She would play a very significant role because she would go to the fetish priest and make offerings and pray to our ancestors. If the ancestors approved of the marriage, she would notify Ruth's father and mother that I wished to marry their daughter.

"Then Ruth's family would have a family council meeting with almost all members of the Adejumo family to decide if my family is acceptable. They would also severely interrogate Ruth. The head of Ruth's family would consult their ancestors, and if the ancestors revealed that it would be a good marriage, they would notify my uncle. Only then would he come personally and ask for the hand of Ruth in marriage. My uncle, accompanied by two or three influential members of the family, would visit Ruth's uncle and her *tanino* to discuss the marriage. They would ask how much the dowry is and would immediately pay the first dowry to cover the cost of the food and liquor to be used in the ceremonies. My uncle would bring two or three bottles of whiskey and pour some of it on the ground to the ancestors. Then those present in this very private ceremony would drink some of the liquor to seal the initial contract. Only a very few influential members of the family would be present for this first secret ceremony. Neither Ruth nor her parents nor my parents would be present.

"Then, later, there would be a public ceremony in which my uncle and *tanino* and other members of my family would publicly thank Ruth's family for allowing her to become part of my family. Before this ceremony, my parents and Ruth's parents would notify every one of the relatives on both sides of the families and invite them to attend this public ceremony. On the prescribed day, the delegation from my family would arrive singing and bringing gifts for the dowry. Ruth's family would at first politely refuse the gifts, but Ruth would come out and settle the question by accepting the dowry. Ruth's family would open the bottle of liquor, pour some of it on the ground for the ancestors, and serve the rest to the family members present. They would again pray to the ancestors of both families to make sure that the marriage is acceptable not only to the living, but to the dead. It is only after this that Ruth would be betrothed to me and the wedding plans could proceed."

Throughout Jean-Marc's account of the Fon customs, Deacon Oke continuously nodded his head in agreement. When he finished, Deacon Oke smiled widely and exclaimed: "Amazing, just amazing. I felt sure that the customs of the Fon would be similar to those of the Yoruba, but I did not realize how much alike they are until hearing your story," he said. "The procedure is virtually the same among the Yoruba, with a few minor differences; but the process is similar."

Then his smile left as he continued. "The problem is that the head of your clan lives in Gomé, and the head of Ruth's family lives in Iwo, and they have no way of knowing whether or not this marriage will be acceptable. But there is a way, and here is what I propose.

"I will offer my services," he suggested, "to fulfill the role normally assumed by the uncle of the bride, and I will offer my wife's services for the role of what you Fon call the *tanino*. I will write Pastor Isaac of Iwo Baptist Church and

*Stained glass window at Yoruba-speaking Baptist
church in Lomé, Togo*

ask him to contact the head of the Adejumo family. He will know the right things to say and do, and he will, like myself, avoid all fetishism and prayers to the ancestors.

"Since Adejumo Samuel and his family are Christians, they do not drink liquor. We will substitute mineral water for the liquor used in the ceremonies. It is extremely important that you provide 40 large kola nuts as part of the dowry, for it is the kola nut among the Yoruba which signifies the official announcement of the engagement. I will also offer my services and those of my wife to the Adejumo family in investigating your family. I will need to write a letter to the head of your clan in Gomé, and your father must present this letter to him unopened. Every question in the letter must be answered in writing and given to me by your father when he returns. I will then forward the responses to the pastor in Iwo, who will relay it to the head of the Adejumo family. After receiving this letter, they will set the price of the dowry."

Then Jean-Marc asked the crucial question, one that had bothered him ever since he decided he wanted to ask for Ruth's hand in marriage. "How much do you think the bride price will be?"

"That I can't say," Deacon Oke responded. "I will do my best to try to influence the family to keep the dowry price as low as possible. I know you are a student and that you come from a family that has little wealth; but Samuel is a wealthy trader, and his family will probably set the price higher than you can really afford to pay. Remember, the dowry goes not just to Ruth's parents, but to the entire family. I feel certain that if Samuel and Ibiyemi were setting the price of the dowry, it would be much lower than the price demanded by the head of the clan. In addition to the bride price, you will need to follow Yoruba customs and include as a part of the dowry a fine piece of cloth for a new suit for Samuel, a large covering cloth, a head tie, some alligator pepper, several bottles of mineral water, and of course, the 40 kola nuts.

"When your father arrives in Lomé," Deacon Oke continued, "Let me know. My wife and I will invite you and your father, and Samuel, Ibiyemi, and Ruth to our home for dinner. After dinner, you and Ruth should arrange to go somewhere so that my wife and I can talk alone with your father and Ruth's parents. By then, I hope I will have heard from the pastor in Iwo so that I can play my role as negotiator properly."

Jean-Marc's head was swimming with all the details that had to be worked out as he climbed onto the back of Deacon Oke's motor scooter and rode back with him to the dormitory. All the way, he prayed that God would clear the path for him to marry the girl he loved so much.

V

Three weeks later, Zukono arrived, hot and exhausted after the trip from Dakar to Lomé. He had traveled by train from Dakar southeast to Bamako, the capital of Mali, and then overland by bus southeast to Bobo-Dioulasso in the southwestern part of Upper Volta. There he had again boarded a train and gone all the way south to Bouaké and across into Ghana from Abengourou. From there he went by bus to Kumasi and then to Accra, Ghana, and finally across the Atlantic coastline into Lomé. The overland route from Dakar to Lomé was far more exhausting to travel than the way Jean-Marc had come.

When they met at the *gare*, Zukono hugged his son with joy and seemed happier than Jean-Marc had seen him in years. There was a sense of freedom in his father's spirit that he had not noticed before. Zukono seemed genuinely impressed with the school's campus and with all that Jean-Marc showed him of the city. Never once did he show any signs of disappointment in Jean-Marc or disapproval of his theological study.

Jean-Marc told him of his adventures in Upper Volta, and Zukono smiled in approval of Jean-Marc's desire to help Joseph and the people of Upper Volta who were suffering so much. Jean-Marc proudly introduced his father to missionaries Holt, Horne, McCall, and Bond.

"There are so many friends that I want you to meet," Jean-

Marc told his father. "I've made friends with several Yoruba people, and the deacon of the Yoruba church I have visited many times has invited you and me to dinner at his home tomorrow night along with another family."

Zukono, of course, had no reason to be reluctant to accept the invitation because he had no idea of the hidden agenda involved. But that night as they sat together eating, Zukono could tell what might be coming. All he had to do was to look at Jean-Marc when Ruth flashed those beautiful eyes, and he knew that his son was in love. He suspected what came later after Jean-Marc and Ruth excused themselves to go out on the porch to listen to the transistor radio.

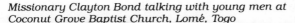
Missionary Clayton Bond talking with young men at
Coconut Grove Baptist Church, Lomé, Togo

Deacon Oke was extremely careful not to say too much nor to overplay his role. He began by saying to Zukono: "It is obvious to Samuel and Ibiyemi that Jean-Marc and Ruth are very much in love and would like to be married, but they are aware of the difficulties in arranging a marriage between young people of different tribes. I have volunteered my services and the services of my wife as *tanino,* and I have contacted the head of the Adejumo clan in Iwo, near Ibadan, to find out if such a marriage would be acceptable to the Adejumo family. I understand you and Jean-Marc are leaving in two days to visit your family in Gomé, and I would like for you to take this sealed letter to the head of your clan. The letter asks a series of very important questions that must be answered to the satisfaction of the Adejumo family before any discussions concerning this matter can proceed further.

"I have made discreet inquiries concerning the betrothal and marriage customs of the Fon and have discovered that they are almost identical to the customs of the Yoruba. I assure you that in these matters I will be careful that we observe the customs and traditions of both tribes. All will be done properly and in good taste. You and Samuel both know that I cannot ask you for permission for this marriage to take place. All I can ask is that you take the letter to the head of your family in Gomé and return his response to me in writing. Then and only then can we discuss the matter personally. Do you agree with the plan I have proposed?"

Zukono acknowledged that he had reservations about his son's marrying a Yoruba, adding that he felt sure that Samuel and Ibiyemi had reservations about their daughter's marrying a Fon. "But the procedure you have proposed is right and proper, and we as parents cannot really discuss this matter together until the heads of our families have considered the proposal. I will do what you have asked," Zukono said.

When he left the home of Deacon Oke that night, he was genuinely impressed with Samuel and Ibiyemi, as well as with Ruth; but he still did not want his only Fon son marrying a Yoruba. He would have to have a long talk with Jean-

Marc as they traveled and with his brother once they arrived in Gomé.

He did not agree with the choice of a Yoruba girl as his son's wife, but he could not quarrel with the process Deacon Oke had proposed in deciding the question. It all depended on what would happen in Gomé.

part three

Beginning in Benin

THE ROAD TO GOMÉ

I

I T WAS THE DAY before Jean-Marc
and Zukono were to leave for Benin.
Jean-Marc went to work at the hotel
restaurant in order to have one more
day's wages in his pay envelope. While
he was at work, Zukono made a visit
that he kept secret from his son.

Zukono walked down the street near
the seminary asking passersby if there
were any Fon in the area. He found a
Fon woman washing clothes in a tub
outside a house nearby and learned
from her that several Fon diviners lived
adjacent to the sacred Forest of Bé. She
reminded Zukono that most of the
diviners and priests in the forest itself
were Ewe, not Fon, and told him to ask
specifically for Bokono, the best of the
Fon diviners.

Crossing the bridge over the lagoon

A spirit abode at a temple in Abomey, Benin

by bus, Zukono stopped near the Forest of Be and began to ask for Bokono. He finally found him in a hut a few hundred meters from the forest.

Zukono explained to Bokono his situation. "My only Fon son has become a follower of the French God called Jesus (to Zukono, anything not African was probably French), and now he wants to marry a Yoruba girl who is also a Christian." I want you to cast the kernels and tell me what the future holds for my son. Specifically, I want to know if it is his destiny to marry the Yoruba girl or if it is his destiny to marry a Fon girl according to the traditions of my clan."

Bokono shook his head. "It will not be possible to do this right," he said, a frown creasing his brow. "To determine *his* future, your son must be present. I could determine *your* destiny but not your son's. All I can do is cast the kernels and see if they will tell me about your destiny and if you are to have grandchildren. I'm not sure if I can determine if your grandchildren will be Fon of Fon."

After reaching an agreement on price, Bokono began to cast the kernels. Taking 16 palm kernels in his right hand, he transferred the kernels four times rapidly from right hand to. left hand, holding them over a rectangular wooden tray on which white meal had been sprinkled. His hands moved so fast Zukono couldn't really tell what he was doing, but Bokono watched closely to see if one or two kernels were left in one of his hands as he transferred the seeds from hand to hand. Each time he saw a seed, he made a double line in the white meal sprinkled on the wooden tray; and each time he saw two seeds left, he made a single line. Eight times he repeated the process, marking on the meal board 16 different combinations of single or double marks. Each mark had a different meaning, and each mark symbolized a specific Fon legend. There were 240 major combinations and the diviner had to know each legend and what it meant. Each of the 16 different marks on the board also had a specific name and meaning.

Zukono did not understand how it worked, but he was convinced that it did. Many times in the past he had gone to the diviner to learn what would happen in the future. Each time the diviner's prediction had come true.

Zukono watched in silence as Bokono cast the kernels and marked the combinations in the meal on his wooden board. When he finished, Bokono put down the kernels, closed his eyes, and raised both hands to the sky. Softly whispering words in a secret language Zukono did not understand, Bokono then looked back at the wooden tray and stared at the marks in absolute silence and total concentration for several minutes. It seemed like hours to Zukono, but he did not dare move or make a sound that might break the spell.

After what seemed like an eternity, Bokono looked up. "You will be the grandfather of two boys and a girl," he announced. "But I cannot tell if these grandchildren will be full-blooded Fon or a mixture of Fon and Yoruba. Without both your son and the girl present, it is impossible to tell. I'm sorry."

Dejected and disappointed, Zukono asked if there were anything he could do to prevent the betrothal of his son to the Yoruba girl.

"You need to go to a *voduno* (chief priest) in order to do that," Bokono said. "The *voduno* can prepare a *gbo* (fetish) especially to prevent betrothal and marriage against the parents' wishes. You will, of course, need to go to a *voduno* of the *Gou* since that is the god of your ancestors."

Zukono nodded in agreement and made plans to see the chief priest in Gomé as soon as he could. If he could not know through divination whether it was Amasou's destiny to marry a Fon girl or the Yoruba girl Ruth, at least he could take steps to prevent him from marrying. He would use the power of the fetish.

II

On their last night together, Jean-Marc and Ruth splurged and went to the *Opéra*, one of Lomé's two air-conditioned cinema houses to see the French-language version of *Le Son du Musique* ("The Sound of Music"). To Jean-Marc and Ruth, it was the most beautiful movie they had ever seen, a rare exception to the smut and trash usually displayed on the screen.

After the movie, they walked hand in hand down the *Rue du Commerce,* soon turning south toward the palm-studded, sandy beaches. As they sat on one of the many benches that lined the wide, white waterfront, they watched a big full moon peek between the palm branches and clouds, and drop slowly toward the *Golfe de Guinée,* as that section of the Atlantic is called. The roar of the waves melted into the background as the whispers of the two young lovers made all of nature's beauty fade into oblivion.

Although their non-Christian friends would never believe it, Ruth and Jean-Marc had no difficulty controlling their physical desires, even in the romantic setting of the beautiful beach. Their love was too deep, too special to mar it with shame and guilt. Yet their friends, even some at church, didn't comprehend the depth of this love fortified as it was by Christian principles. They assumed Jean-Marc and Ruth enjoyed the same physical intimacy that most African young couples who planned to be married practiced.

As they watched the moon descend toward the white-capped waves, Jean-Marc and Ruth whispered in hushed tones not so much about their love for each other, but about their dreams for the future.

"When we are married, Ruth, I would like to have at least three children—two daughters and a son," Jean-Marc confided. "And the daughters will be just as beautiful as you."

Ruth smiled. "I, too, have always wanted to have three children; but I want two sons and one daughter—and the sons will be strong and intelligent like their father."

"We won't argue over our children even before they are born," Jean-Marc cautioned, "especially since we have no control over whether our children will be boys or girls. We will be happy with whatever children God gives to us."

"Where would you like to make our home?" Ruth asked. "When you finish with your studies, wouldn't it be nice to stay here in the Lomé area where we could be close to our friends, Pastor Holt, Deacon Oke, and my parents? I think I would like that."

His brow furrowed with concern, Jean-Marc looked into Ruth's face and reminded her of his plans. "You've heard my testimony. You know that God has called me to proclaim the gospel to the people of Timbuktu. I can do nothing but fulfill the pledge I have made to Pierre, whose dying request was that I promise to take the gospel to his people."

"But, Jean-Marc, you're not serious about actually living and raising a family in Timbuktu, are you? I know you feel God is calling you to be a missionary, but you don't have to go all the way to Timbuktu to be a missionary. You can be a pastor right here in Lomé, or in one of the villages near here. I can't imagine having to live in such a strange and foreign place as Timbuktu. All I know about that place is that a few thousand Muslims and a few thousand goats and cattle live there."

"Ruth, I am serious. It is something I *must* do, not something I *want* to do. God has called me. I have no choice but to follow him. I know it will not be easy, but he never said it would be. But with his strength and help, we can succeed."

"God may have called you to Timbuktu, but he hasn't called me," Ruth snapped. "I can't imagine what life would be like in that barren, desert land. It is nothing like the lush, beautiful city here in Lomé. Trying to rear our children in that harsh, pagan culture would be like trying to make flowers grow in the middle of the desert during dry season. I just don't think I could do it."

"But, Ruth, I couldn't do it without you! I could not cope with the loneliness. I could not be effective as a pastor without you by my side. God has called me, and if God is leading us to become husband and wife, you must submit to God's calling and leadership in my life. It would be your responsibility and duty."

"Jean-Marc, I love you more than words can say, and I want to be your wife. But I don't want to go to Timbuktu. I want to stay here near our friends and family. You can be even more effective as a pastor here than as a missionary in

Timbuktu. Here the people respond to the gospel. When you preach, the people feel God speaking in their hearts. But it would be so much more difficult in the Muslim culture of Timbuktu. They would not respond, and you would become discouraged. I would be even more discouraged. I would not be of help to you; I would be a hindrance."

As they talked, a dark cloud covered the full moon, setting an ominous mood for the moment. The heavy cloud, pushed by the winds of the ocean, moved faster overhead and suddenly erupted in a downpour of rain.

Drenched by the torrents falling from the sky, Jean-Marc and Ruth raced for the nearest building. Hovering beneath an awning, they waited in silence for the next bus. After boarding, they sat staring straight ahead as the bus headed up the *Route de Palime* toward Ruth's home. By the time they arrived, the rain was almost over, with only a few sprinkles trickling from the clouds.

They walked in silence to Ruth's house. As they stood in the courtyard, Jean-Marc turned to Ruth. "Look, I'm sorry we spoiled our last night together before I leave for Benin by arguing. I don't know where God will lead me in the future, but I am certain that God led us together and that it is his will for us to become husband and wife. I love you so much I would do almost anything to marry you. But we both must be open to God's leadership in the future. That's all I ask of you—that you will be open to his will."

"Oh, Jean-Marc, it's my fault. I was the one who spoiled the evening," Ruth confessed. "I do love you, and I do want to be your wife. Right now, I'm being honest when I say I do not want to raise our family in Timbuktu. But I do want to follow God's will, and I do promise to seek his will and follow it."

After they embraced, Jean-Marc and Ruth knelt in the courtyard outside her house and prayed, earnestly seeking God's guidance for their life together in the future.

III

As the *mille kilos* bus bounced along the highway from Lomé to the Benin border, Zukono chuckled silently to himself while Jean-Marc told him about his argument the night before with Ruth. Zukono's poker face showed not a sign of the merriment inside his heart, but he was delighted with what Jean-Marc had confided. Their argument, he believed, was just the sort of wedge the *vodu* would drive between Amasou and Ruth if it were not his son's destiny to marry this girl.

With uncanny wisdom, Zukono knew exactly the right thing to say to drive the wedge even further. "Maybe this is the way that your God is trying to tell you that Ruth is not the right girl for you to marry," he said. "Maybe this argument took place the night before we were to leave to visit Gomé for a good reason. Maybe this God of yours has a good Fon woman picked out for you back in Gomé or Abomey, and it is not your *fa* to marry this Yoruba girl."

Jean-Marc was silent. He didn't argue with his father, but neither did he agree. He knew Zukono would say anything to try to convince him he should marry a Fon rather than a Yoruba. His father's next words reaffirmed his belief.

"That's just like a headstrong Yoruba girl. The Yoruba men have always had trouble with their women. They just don't know their place. A Fon girl would never argue with her man. If her husband wanted to go to Timbuktu or Dakar, or anywhere else in the world, a good Fon wife would follow him without question. She would never question her husband's *fa*. She would obey whether she liked it or not."

Jean-Marc sat silently through his father's speech, knowing it would do no good to argue. He knew that to some extent his father was right. But to him, marrying a Christian girl was far more important than marrying a Fon; and it was *Ruth* he loved. On the other hand, if Ruth's parents knew that he intended to take Ruth to a faraway land, they might never give their permission for the marriage. What *if* Ruth really was not the right girl for him to marry? What *if* his love for her was based not on the fulfillment of God's will, but only on his own selfish desires? What *if* they were married and Ruth refused to go with him to Timbuktu? Would it keep him from fulfilling the vow he had made to Pierre as he lay dying in his arms? Did he love Ruth enough to forsake that calling and vow?

Even though Jean-Marc sat silently and did not share these questions with his father, Zukono smiled to himself as the bus headed toward the border between Togo and Benin. He knew he had said the right things to plant doubts in his son's mind. When they arrived in Gomé, he would see the *voduno* and ask him to cast a spell that would prevent this marriage. Even more important, he would seek out and find a proper Fon girl for his son to marry. His brother would help him find the right girl.

Since both Jean-Marc and Zukono had been born in Benin, they had no difficulty in clearing customs and passing the border checkpoints into Benin. Because the bus had to wait almost two hours for several passengers without proper papers, they were almost three hours late when they arrived in the ancient city of Ouidah, where they got off the Cotonou-bound bus to catch another bus north from Ouidah to Abomey. The road from Ouidah north to Allada was rough and narrow, but it widened to a modern, paved highway from Allada to Bohicon. It was only a short 10 kilometers from Bohicon west to Abomey. When they arrived in Abomey at about seven o'clock on Saturday night, Zukono was amazed at the change.

It had been 17 years since Zukono had seen Abomey, and he was amazed that the city had grown so much. Now more than fifty thousand people lived there, almost double the size of the small city when Zukono had last seen it.

When Zukono and Jean-Marc got off the bus in Abomey, they decided to try to find Zukono's cousin, Grimo, who was a blacksmith in the city. From the *gare*, they walked down the main street toward the area where the blacksmiths worked. About a block from the main market in downtown Abomey, Jean-Marc spotted a building he wanted immediately to visit—the Baptist Center of Abomey, located in a big corner building on a major intersection in downtown Abomey. It was the tallest building in the city. The sign on the building indicated worship services Sunday mornings at

A blacksmith shop in a village in French-speaking West Africa

ten o'clock. He promised himself he would be there early the next morning.

When Zukono reached the area of blacksmith shops, he recognized two ironworkers he had known 17 years earlier. Mase and Siligbo remembered him, too, and greeted him as warmly as if he had never left his homeland.

They said his cousin Grimo was still in Abomey but had left earlier that afternoon. They offered to show Zukono where Grimo lived, for they knew he would want Zukono and Jean-Marc to stay in his home that night.

It was only a short walk to Grimo's compound. When Zukono greeted him, Grimo threw his arms around his cousin and danced with joy that he had returned to Abomey. "You must stay with us tonight and all week," he insisted. "There is so much to tell you about the family. We will need weeks to catch up," he said.

Grimo could not get over the fact that Amasou was now a grown young man. Turning to his own family, Grimo introduced Zukono and Jean-Marc to his two wives and twelve children.

Late into the night, Zukono and Grimo talked about other members of the family. Zukono learned that many of the older members had died and that only his brother and two cousins still lived in the old village of Gomé. Most had scattered throughout Benin, and several had moved to Abidjan and Lomé. Zukono lamented the fact that he had been to both cities but did not know he had relatives there.

Zukono and Grimo planned to spend the entire day Sunday just talking and catching up on what had happened in their lives and in the family in the last 17 years. But Jean-Marc had other plans. He wanted to be at the Baptist center early, long before the services were to begin at 10:00 A.M.

IV

For almost 20 minutes, Jean-Marc walked up and down the street outside the Baptist center, waiting for someone to come and unlock the doors. At about 9:30, a thin young Fon

A reading room at the Baptist center in Abomey, Benin

rode up on a bicycle, put a key into the big padlock, and opened the steel doors that prevented robbers from breaking into the wooden doors inside. Jean-Marc immediately approached the young man.

Greeting him in the Fon language, Jean-Marc introduced himself and told him he was a student at the Baptist Theological School for West Africa in Lomé, Togo. The young man's eyes widened in amazement, for Jean-Marc was the first Fon he had ever known who had gone to Lomé to study for the ministry. He introduced himself as Tchiméoudou Philippe and said he worked for the pastor of the Baptist center, Dutton Bonnell.

"Pastor Bonnell will be here shortly, but he had several things to do before coming here to the center." Speaking in Fon, Philippe asked Jean-Marc why he had come to Abomey, where he had lived before he entered the theological school, and why he had gone there to study for the ministry. It was obvious that he was puzzled that a Fon young man was studying for the ministry at Lomé and no one in Abomey knew about it.

Missionary Dutton A. Bonnell, Jr., draws water from a well dug by missionaries and nationals of Benin

As they walked inside and began to straighten the chairs and get ready for the worship service, Jean-Marc briefly shared his testimony with Philippe, starting with his conversion, his call to the ministry as a result of the death of Pierre, his quest for a theological education, and his reason for this visit to Abomey and Gomé, where he was born.

Philippe stood in awe and wonderment. He was amazed not only at Jean-Marc's story, but at his ability to communicate his feelings in the Fon language. "You must share your testimony with our people here this morning," he insisted. "When Pastor Bonnell arrives, I want to ask him to invite you to give your testimony."

Jean-Marc agreed, saying he would be glad to speak to the people. Just as they finished arranging the chairs, an English-made car similar to a jeep drove up, and a short, strongly built man with an almost bald head got out. He was followed by an even shorter woman with light brown hair. A crowd of children waiting outside the center raced to their sides, and the man and woman hugged many of the children. Joking and teasing the children, the *yovo* (as white men are called in Benin) picked up one little boy, tossed him into the air, caught him, and swung him down beneath his legs. The boy squealed with delight and hugged the man's legs, refusing to let go.

"That's Pastor Bonnell," Philippe said, explaining the obvious.

"Pasteur! Pasteur!" shouted Philippe above the squeal of the children. "There is a visitor you must meet." Then he introduced Jean-Marc and explained who he was and why he was at Abomey.

"Jean-Marc was here even before I was, waiting for someone to arrive," Philippe told the smiling pastor, speaking in French. "God has been at work in his life in a powerful way. He speaks Fon beautifully, and I'm sure the people would be inspired by his testimony."

Pastor Bonnell was delighted and insisted that Jean-Marc give his testimony that morning, either in French or Fon. "If you speak in Fon, you'll have to share your testimony with me in French later," he said. "I've been able to learn only a little Fon during the years I've been here."

Pastor Bonnell introduced Jean-Marc to his wife, Marilyn, and took him to meet several other key leaders in the church. Full of energy and enthusiasm, Bonnell filled the room with joy and happiness. It was obvious that he loved the people and that they loved him. He made it a point to greet personally every person who came to the services, making each one feel special.

Just before the service started, Bonnell invited Jean-Marc into his office for prayer with several of the leaders. Before the prayer session began, he told the leaders about Jean-Marc: "During my nine-year ministry here in Abomey, I have prayed that a Fon young man would feel God's call to the ministry, receive a theological education to prepare himself, and come to Abomey to preach the gospel to his own people in his own language. Today I believe God has answered that prayer in the most unusual way. He has sent to us Jean-Marc, a Fon who accepted Christ in Dakar, Senegal, and who is now a student at the Baptist School of Theology for West Africa in Lomé, Togo.

"Jean-Marc is visiting his cousin here in Abomey and is going to Gomé with his father to visit his uncle and other relatives. I've asked Jean-Marc to share his testimony with our people this morning, but I've had another idea. It wouldn't be fair to ask him to preach the entire sermon this morning, but I wonder, Jean-Marc, if you will preach for us at tonight's service? If you will, I want to tell our people this morning after your testimony that you will preach tonight in the Fon language."

Jean-Marc agreed enthusiastically. He would have been glad to preach that morning too, but he didn't say so.

About 85 people were present at the service. Jean-Marc loved the singing, but what he loved most was being able to share his testimony in the language of his heart. As he spoke, the people responded in a unique way that he'd never experienced before. There were tears in their eyes when he told them of Pierre's dying words. Jean-Marc himself was moved.

even though he had shared his testimony dozens of times previously. When he concluded, there was a silence and a reverence in the room so profound that no one wanted to break the spell.

Because Jean-Marc had spoken in Fon, Bonnell was unable to understand; but Philomene Anani, Bonnell's translator, whispered into the pastor's ear a summary of Jean-Marc's testimony.

When Bonnell got up for the sermon, he praised Jean-Marc for his powerful testimony and announced that Jean-Marc had agreed to preach during the Sunday night service in the Fon language. Following the service, Jean-Marc was swarmed by people wanting to talk to him about his experiences and to thank him for his testimony.

That night when Jean-Marc stood in the pulpit to preach, he had never felt so strongly the power of God's presence, nor had he felt so strongly a bond between pulpit and pew, between preacher and worshipper. It was an experience he would never forget.

THE CURSE OF VODU

I

The walk from Abomey to Gomé was less than 20 kilometers; but for Jean-Marc, it was a walk 200 years back into history. He had been to villages in Togo and Upper Volta, but those were different. Yet if someone had asked him to explain the difference, he would have had great difficulty putting it into words.

It wasn't so much that the villages looked different; it was that they "felt" different. Jean-Marc had "felt" the difference from the moment he arrived in Abomey, but the feelings grew stronger as he walked from Abomey to Gomé.

Ominous. That was the word to describe the feeling, he decided after a great deal of reflection. It was in the atmosphere, permeating the very air he breathed. Its pervasiveness was almost frightening. With a foreboding that was eerie, Jean-Marc knew the visit to Gomé would not be an enjoyable one.

It did not take him long to realize why. It was the power of the fetish. Everywhere he looked, the people were captives of fetish worship. Fetishism was so prevalent that it seemed to smother Jean-Marc, filling the atmosphere like a dense fog that obscures reality and truth. The power of fetishism was real to the people of the Abomey and Gomé area—unquestionably real.

Every compound, almost every house, had a special fetish hut in the courtyard or just outside the compound. Some had tall poles with a long white flag fluttering in the breeze, indicating a fetish hut devoted to the worship of the god Dan, the spirit purported to live in moving water, especially rivers. Symbolically, the god is represented in the form of a snake; and the long, narrow white flags flying on the bamboo poles were like long white snakes waving in the air.

Some of the fetish huts were completely enclosed and made of stucco mud; others were simply four wooden poles supporting a tin roof to keep the sun and rain off the altar underneath the roof. Inside almost every hut was a mound of mud mixed with palm oil that served as the altar for the particular fetish god. The altar was covered with dozens of clay pots, some with the symbol of the snake on the lids. Most of the fetish huts were about four feet wide and deep, and about three feet tall. Some were even large enough for an erect adult to walk inside. As they walked past, Jean-Marc could look inside some huts and see fresh blood or feathers from a chicken that had been offered as a sacrifice that very morning to the fetish god believed to live in the hut.

Some altars were simply big mounds of clay mixed with palm oil, usually laced under a tree. Often there was an

Fetish figure

Objects of fetish worship

earthen pot partially buried in the ground at the altar. Jean-Marc knew from what his father had told him long ago that these were shrines to the god of his ancestors, Gou, the god of iron. The worshippers of Gou believed that he lives in the earth, rather than in the water or the sky like many other Fon gods. They would not put roofs over shrines to Gou for fear that fire (from the forge) would burn them. Surrounding the altars were several sacred *anya* trees where offerings of pottery and bits of iron were scattered on the ground.

An idol with sacrifices placed in clay dishes to the right

Sadness filled Jean-Marc's heart as he walked silently with his father on the narrow dirt path from Abomey to Gomé. People so steeped in ancestor and fetish worship found it terribly difficult to leave the traditions of the past. Jean-Marc yearned for them to know the joy and happiness Jesus could bring them.

As they neared one village, Jean-Marc and Zukono heard ceremonial drums beating, and they knew some sort of sacred rite was in progress. They saw a group of men sitting in the compound watching the *voduno* and the village chief lead a ceremonial rite. Out of respect Zukono stopped, and out of curiosity Jean-Marc watched.

The *voduno* had already made the sacrifice of a chicken, pouring the chicken's blood on the altar of the fetish hut. Some of the chicken feathers had been mixed with the blood and poured on the shaft of a cane tipped with an iron spear. The chicken killed for the ceremony was cooking on a spit over a wood fire in the center of the compound. While Jean-Marc and Zukono watched from a distance, the *voduno* poured more blood on the ground and placed the spear-tipped cane in the blood on the ground. Then he handed to the village chief a special drink in a gold cup. The chief ceremoniously drank the concoction and stepped over the spear-tipped cane lying in the blood on the ground.

Spear, blood, and feathers from a rite of sacrifice

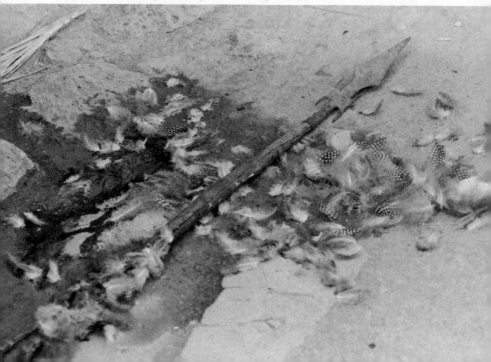

Then the men broke into song, and the women began dancing to the sound of drums. Jean-Marc asked his father in a hushed whisper what the ceremony was all about. His father explained that the people believed the spirit of the man who established the village lived in the wooden shaft of the spear-tipped cane. Once each year they observed a ceremony in which they made a sacrifice to the ancestor who founded the village. The blood poured onto the cane was to appease the spirit of the departed ancestor. Part of the cooked chicken was placed in the earthen pots in the fetish house to feed the spirits of other ancestors.

Jean-Marc shivered as he watched. He firmly believed what he was seeing and feeling was demonic and satanic. With each step they walked beyond that village, Jean-Marc prayed that God would fill him with his spirit and his love and enable him somehow to communicate that love and spirit to the people of his family in Gomé.

II

There was great rejoicing when Zukono and Jean-Marc entered the village of Gomé. Long before they arrived, several young boys who served as lookouts had seen them and alerted the village that strangers were coming. An older man whose duty it was to greet strangers outside the village met them and sent word back with one of the boys that the brother of Ayato, Zukono, who had left the village 17 years ago, was returning home with his son.

Ayato, the head of the clan of ironworkers who lived in Gomé, had become the village chief. When his long-departed brother returned, there was great rejoicing in the village. Zukono was treated like a celebrity, not like an outcast. Even though Zukono had left the village in shame when the people blamed him for the death of his wife, he returned in triumph.

Jean-Marc thought of the story of the Prodigal Son and saw some interesting parallels. Even though Zukono had not wasted his life in riotous living, he was welcomed back to the village just as the father welcomed the prodigal son.

After the customary formal greetings and introductions, Zukono was careful to show several pictures of Narie and their children to his brother and others who had lived there 17 years. The implication was subtle but obvious to Jean-Marc. Zukono was saying, but not in words, that his "seed was not bad," and that he was not really responsible for the death of his wife in childbirth, as people of the village had believed.

Ayato introduced Zukono and Jean-Marc to his four wives and some of his 23 children. As chief of the village and head of the clan of ironworkers of Gomé, Ayato was entitled to more wives than anyone else; consequently, he also had more children. Each wife had her own house, and Ayato took turns sleeping in the four mud brick huts with thatched roofs. To the people of Gomé, there was nothing wrong with polygamy: it was the way of the people.

Soon after Zukono and Jean-Marc arrived, one of Ayato's wives supervised the butchering of a young goat and the preparations for a big feast honoring Zukono and Jean-Marc. Zukono knew there would be singing, dancing, and drinking that night, and that men of the village would talk late into the night about life in Gomé as it was before Zukono left.

In a paradox that Zukono could not explain, everything was the same; yet everything was different about life in the village as he remembered it. While the population of Abomey had almost doubled in the last 17 years, the population of Gomé had been cut almost in half. Judging from the empty huts and the number of children, Zukono estimated that fewer than three hundred people lived in Gomé now compared to well over six hundred 17 years ago.

Also, life in the city had changed Zukono. The village had none of the conveniences of the city that he had come to take for granted. There was no market, but following the custom of the people, many of the people of Gomé walked the 17 kilometers to Abomey every Thursday for market day in the city. Of course, there was no electricity, no refrigeration, no power tools or equipment of any kind, and no automobiles at all. People had a few bicycles, but most of the people walked. No school existed, but there was one white stucco building about 30 meters long—a temple for the worship of Gou.

The welcoming festivities took place that night because the next day was a sacred day for the blacksmiths of Gomé. Following the feast, the men of the village sat under a tree and talked. The center of attention, Zukono, was peppered with questions about life in the big city of Dakar. As anxious as he was to talk, Zukono had great difficulty, however, making the men understand what life in the city was like. He tried to describe the huge airport and the fierce roar of the supersonic jet, the French Concorde, which landed there several times a week. But most of the men in the village had never seen an airplane, much less a supersonic jet. He tried to describe the big freeway and the terrible traffic jams, but few of the men had seen more than a few dozen cars and trucks at one time in Abomey.

But when he tried to describe his work at the nail factory, with its huge open-hearth furnace and big automated ladles for pouring molten steel into the machines that made the nails, Zukono was at a complete loss of words. The ironworkers of Gomé had never worked with molten iron and steel; they only knew how to heat already-tempered steel to pliable temperatures and beat it into new shapes with their hammers and anvils.

Zukono did not feel he was any more intelligent or better educated than the blacksmiths of Gomé; but his experiences had been so different from theirs that he couldn't communicate to them what life was really like in the big city. And he seemed to have forgotten what life was really like in the village.

Jean-Marc was even more frustrated than his father. He had nothing whatever in common with the men of Gomé. There were only two or three young men of his age in the village and none of them had any education at all. When Jean-Marc asked Ayato about this, Ayato hung his head in dismay. "All our young men have gone to the city, where they can get jobs and earn paper money. We have no school here in Gomé, so the young men who want to get an education have to go to Abomey to study. After they once move to the city, they almost never return to the village. Our elders are greatly disturbed for fear the village will die out in another decade or two."

Jean-Marc noticed that there were many more young women of marriageable age in Gomé than there were young men, but obviously none of the young women had received any formal education. There was only one young man, Tosu, who apparently could read and write French, and Ayato depended upon him to translate and read any written document or paper that he received as village chief. There were several men in the village who could speak French, but Tosu was the only one who could read and write it.

Late that night, after the circle of men broke up, Ayato and Zukono wandered off to Ayato's private hut to talk alone. Zukono and his brother sat under a tree outside Ayato's private hut where Ayato knew they would not be disturbed. "Tell me, my brother," said Ayato, "why did you come back to Gomé after so many long years? And why did you wait so long to return?"

"There is a purpose to my visit," replied Zukono. "Until now, I felt I could not afford the expense of a long trip from Dakar to Gomé; but because of my son, everything is different. All my life I have saved as much as I could of what I earned working at the nail factory so that my son could go to the university and someday return to our homeland as a government worker. But in the last few years, my son has given me nothing but grief."

Zukono told the story of Jean-Marc's conversion to Christianity, his desire to become a missionary to the people of his "best friend" in Timbuktu, and his trip to Lomé to enter the Baptist School of Theology for West Africa.

"But now, to top it all off, my son believes he has fallen in love with a Yoruba girl from Lomé, and he wants to marry her. Her people are Christians. They worship in a place called a church; and when I arrived in Lomé, a leader in the church, who is acting in behalf of Amasou and the girl, presented me with a letter to deliver to you as the head of our clan. This man's wife is acting as *tanino* in the fulfillment of Yoruba and Fon betrothal customs. The letter asks you to answer a number of detailed questions about our family background. Deacon Oke, as he is called, told me to get your responses in writing and bring the reply to him when I return to Lomé."

Zukono handed the unopened letter to Ayato. Ayato agreed to answer the questions fully and truthfully, pointing out that he would have to get Tosu's help in reading, translating, and writing his responses to the letter. "Although I will respond truthfully to every question, tell me first how you feel about this proposed marriage. Do you approve?"

"Of course not," replied Zukono. "Amasou is my only son who is a full-blooded Fon. I naturally want him to marry a good Fon girl. I do not want my son to become a missionary for the white man's God to the people of Timbuktu. I want my son to return to our homeland and become a government worker."

Ayato nodded his understanding and agreement but offered no solution to Zukono's problem. They sat in silence for a few moments before Zukono asked his brother: "What do you advise me to do? What can I do to stop this marriage? How can I influence my son to return to our country to become a government worker?"

"At dawn tomorrow," replied Ayato, "you must go to the shrine of Gou and worship with the people. There will be a special ceremony tomorrow for three new initiates into the cult of Gou *vodunsi* (members of a special sacred order who undergo a long period of initiation before they can become members). Since you are not a *vodunsi* yourself, normally you would not attend this ceremony. But your problem needs special power, and the power of the *vodu* will be present tomorrow. I will talk to the chief priest tonight and you will be welcome as a special guest for this ceremony.

"After you have worshipped, you must talk to Dosu Togbo —the chief priest of the worshippers of the Gou—and seek his advice. Do whatever he tells you to do. He will direct you in what sacrifice to make to Gou, and as the *voduno* of our people, he will make a *gbo* (fetish) to prevent this marriage.

"But that is not enough. We must somehow convince Amasou that it is better for him to marry a Fon and return to our country. We must find for him an attractive job that he cannot afford to turn down. My third wife has a cousin in Cotonou who is the adjutant to the chief of staff of the *Service Civique* (civil service) in the Benin government. On your return to Lomé, you should visit him. Ask him to help find a job in the government for Amasou. I will write a letter of introduction, but first you must see the *voduno*. Amasou's life is in the hands of the gods."

Missionary W. Neville Claxon talking with a fertility cult priest

III

The pulsating beat of ceremonial drums awakened Zukono before sunup, and he made his way immediately to the temple of Gou near the sacred forest not far from the village. The temple was a white-clay brick building with a portico along the front wall. It was about 30 meters by 10 meters. A walled-off area behind the temple included a cult house where the candidates for initiation into the *vodunsi,* as the cult is called, lived during their initiation period.

About 25 or 30 people, most of them family members of the candidates for initiation, sat or stood outside the temple waiting for the ceremonies to begin. At the far left of the temple, three drummers were beating the symbolic rhythm of the earth gods, the sons of Mawu and Lisa.

Precisely at sunrise, Dosu Togbo, the chief priest of Gou, walked out of the temple in his full regalia and spoke briefly to the people, introducing the initiates.

Then the chief priest began to recount the legend of the coming of Gou and Agé to earth, retelling a version of the Mawu story everyone present knew but never tired of hearing.

"From her place in the sky, Mawu, the creator of the earth, saw that things were not going well on earth and that men had no way of cultivating the land or building houses because they had no tools of any kind. Mawu sent her only son, Lisa, to the earth to help mankind. In Lisa's hand, Mawu placed a sword—not like the ones the Fon use today—but it resembled a sword and was called *gugbasa.* Mawu told Lisa to show human beings how to use the metal to make tools to till the land, clear the forests, and build houses for their people. Mawu told Lisa to explain that without metal, humanity could not survive. Mawu was so pleased with the response to Lisa's instructions that Mawu gave to Lisa the sun, where he could watch over the universe. Later they had sons. Their fourth was named Gou, god of war. Gou is not iron, but the property of iron which gives it the power to cut. Gou is the personification of all the human skills which involve the use of metal, like making swords and guns. It is the task of Gou to make the earth habitable for people.

"Agé, the hunter, is the fifth son of Mawu and Lisa. He is god of the bush; the animals are under his control. He gives the knowledge and ability to hunt. It is Agé who guides our people to find food. While Gou gives man the weapons with which to hunt, it is Agé who enables man to find the game.

"In honor of Gou and Agé, whom we worship today, let the initiation ceremony begin!"

The drums beat wildly as the priest turned quickly and strode back into the temple, entering through the east portico door. Then followed an initiation ritual that included some of the most vivid and secret aspects of ritualistic sacrifice.

When the candidates appeared, each danced as if in a trance. Perspiring profusely as they danced, the candidates never once missed a step or a beat. On the head of each was a

A palm forest in Benin

small red pot covered with strands of cowrie shells, and blue, white, and black beads. In addition to balancing the pot on their heads, they held in their mouths three strands of cowrie shells, each string containing the sacred number of 41 cowries.

Finally, the procedure reached the point where three mats were spread for the candidates. Each time a mat was placed on the ground, the priestess placing the mat raised and lowered it five times. Finally, the candidates were seated on the mats at the east end of the temple, and the red pots were taken from their heads and placed at their feet. After a brief period of rest, the candidates danced three times in a procession around the temple, stopping each time at the shrines dedicated to Mawu, Lisa, Gou, and Agé. After they completed the circle around the temple three times, the candidates were lifted by two men and carried into the enclosed courtyard where the cult house was located. When this happened, the relatives of each candidate bent down and kissed the earth, throwing sand from the ground into their faces, arms, and chests.

By then, it was past ten o'clock in the morning, and there was a brief intermission in the ceremonies. While the relatives and guests talked and the children played, the candidates were inside the cult house preparing for the next part of the initiation ceremony. About 30 minutes later, new mats were spread in front of the temple, each raised and lowered five times before being placed on the ground. Finally, the chief priest announced that it was time for the final ceremony, the shaving of the heads.

First, the three candidates' heads were washed. Then, using razors made by blacksmiths who were members of the cult, the chief priest and his priestesses shaved the heads bald. When the shaving was completed, sacrifices were made.

Togbo, the chief priest, took a chicken that was brought to him and gently stroked it three times. Tucking the chicken's head underneath its wing, he suddenly threw the chicken to the ground, stunning it. He plucked three feathers from the bird, and then twisted its head and pulled out its tongue.

Moving quickly, the chief priest held the bleeding neck of the chicken over the bodies of the three candidates, allowing several drops of blood to fall on the head, big toe, thigh, back, breasts, lips, palms, and on the thumb of each hand. On the shaved head of each candidate, a feather was placed in the quickly coagulating blood.

Then the hair that had been shaved from the head of each candidate was placed on a white cloth. Some of the blood from the chicken was sprinkled on the hair. Then the fingernails and toenails, which had been clipped earlier from each candidate, were added to the three white cloths. The three white cloths were folded neatly and taken inside the temple where they were to be preserved. Zukono knew that by preserving the hair and nail clippings, the priests would be able to retain their supernatural control over the members of the cult, for hair and nail clippings are often used whenever a curse is placed on anyone by the *voduno*.

After the completion of the sacrifice and their ceremony of shaving the heads, the three candidates were led dancing back into the cult house. As the songs and beat of the drums continued, everyone knew that the climax was about to take place. Suddenly, several members of the Gou cult appeared from the cult house, swinging between them a big sack that was long and heavy. Three times the men ran around the shrine, swinging the white sheet and its heavy contents to and fro as they ran. Finally, the bundle was placed in front of the temple of Agé on a mat that had been laid there earlier. An old priestess shook her rattle beside the bundle while the drums beat louder. Suddenly, the initiate leaped from beneath the white sheet and began to dance in a violent frenzy.

Neither of the two other candidates repeated the act, but shortly afterwards, all three candidates came outside and danced an even more frenzied dance. The relatives threw coins at their feet, and the money was gathered by the priests. Finally, the ceremonies over, the candidates retired to

Missionary Dutton A. Bonnell, Jr., walking with men to a village in Benin

180

BEGINNING IN BENIN

the cult house and the guests and relatives left. By then it was
mid-afternoon.

While everyone else departed, Zukono waited beneath a
tree, hoping that Togbo would soon come out of the temple. It
had been a busy day for the chief priest, but Zukono needed
badly to see him. All he could do, however, was wait and
hope.

IV

Despite the distant beat of the drums, Jean-Marc slept late
that Tuesday morning. He was tired from the long journey
and was already bored in Gomé. Arising about ten o'clock in
the morning, he walked around the village just to observe the
way the people lived.

Even though there were no modern conveniences like
those in the city, the people seemed to be happy. "Ignorance
is bliss," thought Jean-Marc to himself sarcastically. He regretted thinking it almost immediately, for he knew that the
people of Gomé were not ignorant. Uneducated, yes; but ignorant, no.

Jean-Marc approached a well with a hand pump where
several young girls were filling big buckets with water. He
noticed three young men seated under a tree watching the
girls and laughing. He walked up to the young men and tried
to start a conversation.

After going through the traditional Fon greetings, he told
the three young men: "I am Zukono Jean-Marc. What are
your names?"

"We know who you are," replied one young man. His tone
was cold, indifferent, implying that he already knew who
Jean-Marc was and didn't care whether Jean-Marc knew
who they were. The other two youths, both younger, did not
volunteer their names either, but Jean-Marc heard one of
them refer to the older youth as Bosu.

Jean-Marc tried to start a conversation with the young
men, but he really didn't know what to say. "What do you do
here for entertainment?" he asked.

"Nothing," replied Bosu. "Just sit around and watch the

girls, even if they aren't worth watching. We go to Abomey when we want to do anything."

"Do you go to school?"

"There is no school here. Agasu here," said Bosu pointing to the youngest boy, "used to go to school in Abomey, but he quit."

Seeking an opportunity to witness to the young men, Jean-Marc asked, "Did you ever go to church in Abomey?"

"What do you mean?" asked Bosu. "What is church?"

Surprised that the young man had never heard of church, Jean-Marc replied, "It's the place where you go to worship God and his son, Jesus Christ."

"Who is Jesus? I've never heard of him. Is he one of the sons of Mawu and Lisa?"

Jean-Marc explained who Jesus is, and how he came into the world to enable mankind to know and understand God and to cleanse men of their sins. He tried to use the simplest words he could to explain salvation, but he soon began to realize that the young men just didn't understand. Most of all, they didn't care.

About that time the most attractive young girl in the village came to the well to pump water into her bucket, and the boys quickly changed the subject. The three young men at the well shouted at the girl and flirted, but she paid them no attention.

Apparently the three boys had been waiting at the well for the girl because when she filled her bucket and started to walk back to her compound, the three boys followed. Bosu offered to carry her water bucket, but she ignored him. Jean-Marc stood in the shade of the tree and watched as the girl and her three male admirers walked off.

In dismay he turned back toward the hut where he had slept the night before. He felt discouraged because he had so much difficulty communicating with the people. His experiences had been so radically different from those of the people in the villages that they had very little in common. He felt his efforts in witnessing had been a dismal failure.

As he wandered through the village, Jean-Marc heard the

beat of the drums intensify. He decided to investigate and followed the sound to the temple, arriving just before the ceremony of shaving the heads of the candidates was to begin. In the crowd of about 50 people, he saw his father seated in the shade of the tree. When the chief priest had finished shaving the head of the third candidate, Jean-Marc watched as the sacrifice began. His face frozen in horror, Jean-Marc stared at the unbelievable scene when Togbo twisted off the chicken's head and pulled out its tongue. A chill went up his spine when he watched the priest hold the bleeding chicken over the heads of the three candidates, sprinkling the blood over their bodies.

When the one rose and danced in the trance-like frenzy, Jean-Marc could watch no longer. He walked off in utter dismay and frustration. He knew the power of fetishism that had a strong hold on the people was beyond his comprehension. The candidate, staring blankly into space totally unaware of what was happening, seemed to be possessed by a demon.

All the way back to the village, Jean-Marc prayed, asking God to enable him to reach out to these people with the love of Jesus. He felt completely out of place in Gomé. But if he, who had been born in this village, had difficulty communicating the gospel to the people, how could anyone ever reach them? The question gnawed inside him the entire time he was there.

V

Zukono waited almost an hour before Togbo, the chief priest, came out of the temple and approached him. While he waited, Zukono became more and more impatient, but he knew that he could not enter the temple on the day that candidates for the *vodunsi* were being initiated. This was a privilege reserved only for the initiated cult members.

Togbo greeted Zukono like an old friend, even though it had been 17 years since they had seen each other. Zukono wasn't sure whether Togbo remembered him or just knew from Ayato that he was coming. The two men went through the long list of traditional Fon greetings before they finally got down to business. At last, Togbo asked, "What can I do for you?"

Zukono explained the problem in detail, summarizing the tensions with Amasou during the past few years which culminated in his desire to marry the Yoruba girl. "Is there a *gbo* that you can make that will prevent my son from marrying this girl? And is there a *gbo* that can make my son change his mind about becoming a missionary for the white man's God and instead become a government worker to help our people?"

"No," replied Togbo quickly. "There are no such *gbos* designed for these particular problems specifically. But perhaps I can help by making two *gbos* for you that you can apply generally to the problems you are facing.

"You will have to go to the market in Abomey on Thursday to buy the ingredients for these two *gbos* because I do not have the ingredients here in Gomé. It will take several days, but I will try to make them for you as quickly as possible."

Then he described in detail the two *gbos* and how they could be used. The first was called a *yewome*, and it was designed to help the possessor prevail in any quarrel. Togbo described it as a white pendant worn on a string about the neck. After a quarrel, the *gbo* could be activated by spraying strong liquor from the mouth of the owner three times over the charm, placing it about the neck, and calling its name, *yewome*, three times.

"You will need to go to the fetish market in Abomey and buy the following items for this *gbo*," instructed Togbo. "I will need the heart of a cat, the leaves of the akpaku bean plant, the string for the pendant, and the white pod of a special small gourd in which the heart and leaves are placed."

Togbo explained that the heart of a cat is used in the *gbo* because of the old Fon proverb which says, "If a cat goes into a house and a rat is there, the cat does not ask permission to catch her prey." The leaves of the bean are placed inside the pendant because the beanstalk climbs the pole "without asking permission to do so," he explained.

"The second *gbo* is more difficult to make, and even more powerful," Togbo said. "It can perform evil as well as good. It can protect you while you sleep, and it can drive an enemy to insanity.

"Since Amasou is your only Fon son, you probably will not want to use this *gbo* against him; but it can be used against the Yoruba girl. If she were suddenly to go insane, it is doubtful that your son would want to marry her," he explained.

Giving him detailed instructions on what to buy at the fetish market, Togbo listed the following items needed for this *gbo*: a piece of wood about 12 to 18 inches long and 3 inches square from the rozo liana tree, about 3 feet of special *gbo* cord made specifically to tie pieces of a *gbo* together, the skull of a small monkey, the leaves of the *zama* bush, several bits of sacred pottery used in the worship of Gou, and seven peppers.

Then Togbo told Zukono how to activate this *gbo* and warned him of the misuse of its power. First, a chicken must be sacrificed to the *vodu*, and its blood poured over the *gbo*. Then seven peppers and some strong drink are rubbed into the eyes of the human figure carved by the *voduno* from the piece of wood. Then the name of the person on whom the curse is made is called, and the *voduno* who casts the spell pronounces the secret words. Immediately the person on whom the curse is made goes insane. This madness, however, lasts only three days. If permanent insanity is desired, the curse must be repeated on the third day.

His curiosity aroused, Zukono asked Togbo to describe what the *gbo* would look like when it was finished. "From the special wood, I will carve a human figure about 12 to 18 inches tall. The bottom of the *gbo* will be sharpened to a point so that it can be stuck into the ground or into an altar. Around the arms and chest of the *gbo*, I will place part of the skull of the monkey, the bits of sacred pottery, and the leaves of the *zama* bush. The *gbo* cord will be wrapped around each of these things, securing them tightly to the torso and arms of the carved figure."

Warning that this was an especially powerful *gbo*, Togbo added that the curse could be intensified by pounding the pointed, sharpened base of the *gbo* into the ground or into the altar by hitting the head of the carved human figure seven times. "At the end of seven days, the person on whom the curse is placed will die, provided the whole procedure is repeated on the third day."

Zukono smiled, for these were exactly the kinds of fetish charms that he needed to protect not only his son's future, but the future of his own family. After all, Amasou was his only Fon son.

APPOINTMENT IN ABOMEY

 Jean-Marc was so bored and felt so out of place that he didn't want to stay another day in Gomé. When Zukono told him he was going to Abomey with Ayato on Thursday for market day, Jean-Marc asked to go along.

For Zukono, market day in Abomey was like a big convention. People from villages all around Abomey came into the city to sell their wares in the market. It didn't seem to matter if they didn't sell much. The most important thing seemed to be seeing their friends. Zukono saw several older men and women he had known and enjoyed visiting with them. He was especially proud to be seen with his brother, Ayato, the village chief of Gomé. On the other hand, Ayato seemed to be genuinely proud of his brother, Zukono, who had travelled to faraway places that others had only heard about.

While Zukono visited in the market and shopped secretly for the fetish items the priest had instructed him to buy, Jean-Marc went to the Baptist center.

When Jean-Marc arrived at the Baptist center, there was a crowd of about 80 children inside, seated in four rows of chairs. Like children everywhere, they were loud and playful; but they were orderly and disciplined at the same time. Just

A market scene in Abomey, Benin

after Jean-Marc walked into the room, Marilyn Bonnell walked out of the small office that adjoined the large room used as a place of worship. She called one of the children, and a young boy about nine years of age went with her into the office.

While 80 pairs of brown eyes watched, Jean-Marc followed Marilyn. He watched with interest as she and her translator, Felicienne Adjinon, asked the boy to bend over. Then a nurse, Henrietta Bodmard, gave him an injection in the fleshy part of his back.

Without a whimper or a tear, the young boy marched back to his seat, and Marilyn Bonnell turned to call the next patient. When she saw Jean-Marc for the first time, her eyes lit up. "Jean-Marc! You have come back to help us!"

Jean-Marc confessed that he did not even know something was going on at the center, but he had come to Abomey for market day with his father and wanted to stop by the center. "What are you doing here today giving shots to all these children?" he asked.

Jean-Marc learned that once each month, the Baptist center sponsored a free immunization program for the children who attended the weekly Bible study sessions. "We have about 180 children who regularly receive shots here at the center. In addition, we've just started a family health program for all ages, with meetings once each month. Madame Bodmard is teaching the adults basic health care and hygiene in the Fon language, with about 40 adults involved."

Apologizing for not having time to talk longer about what they were doing, Marilyn Bonnell asked if Jean-Marc had time to stay and help. "We're almost through giving the shots, but in a few moments we will give the children bread and milk, and we will need some help serving them."

Jean-Marc was delighted to stay. When all the immunization shots had been given, the children sang some choruses. After they had sung for about 15 minutes, they went outside and played some games. While Marilyn Bonnell led the children in the games in the courtyard, Jean-Marc helped Philippe rearrange the chairs and set up tables in the large

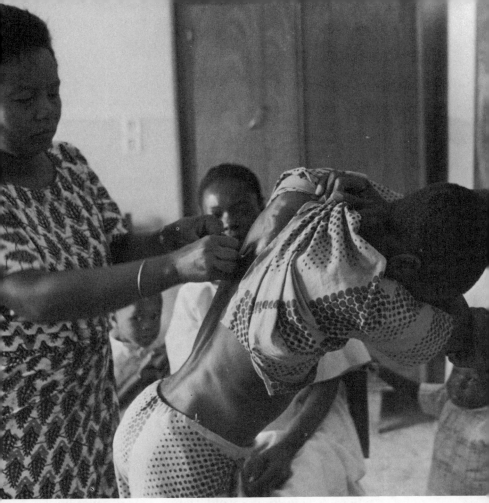

A youth receiving an immunization shot from Felicienne Adjinon, a nurse at the Baptist center, Abomey, Benin

room the children had just left. As they were setting up the tables and chairs, the women got the paper cups, pitchers of cold milk, and loaves of bread ready. After the play period was over, the children came back inside and hungrily ate the bread and drank the cold milk.

For many of the children, it was the only time they got to drink cold milk. Most of the children don't get much protein in their diet, and the protein-enriched bread and milk help counteract the imbalance in their diet, Marilyn explained.

About that time, Dutton Bonnell came into the center and was just as surprised and delighted as his wife to see Jean-Marc. "How long can you stay in Abomey?" he asked immediately. "Can you stay until Sunday and preach for us on Sunday morning?"

Thrilled with the opportunity, Jean-Marc said he would talk to his father and uncle and see if they would object to his staying in Abomey until Monday. If they demanded that he return to Gomé, he would simply get up early Sunday morning and walk into the city in time for the services.

Philippe immediately invited Jean-Marc to stay in his home until Monday. "There is so much I want to ask you," he said, insisting that Jean-Marc accept his invitation.

Jean-Marc walked to the market to find his father. At first Zukono balked when Jean-Marc asked if he or Ayato would be offended if he remained in Abomey until Monday. But Ayato overheard his nephew's request and insisted that Jean-Marc accept Philippe's invitation. Finally Zukono relented and agreed.

II

It was almost twilight when Zukono and Ayato finally started home from Abomey. For Zukono, the visit to the market, where he saw so many old friends, was the highlight of his entire visit.

"Why don't you move back to Gomé?" Ayato asked Zukono as they walked on the narrow, dusty path toward Gomé.

"I've seriously considered it," Zukono replied. "I've even thought of divorcing Narie and just staying here in my homeland. I think I could find work, maybe in Abomey at one of the blacksmith shops. But I'm afraid there would not be enough work for me in Gomé."

Zukono didn't say so but he was afraid he might not be happy living in the village. For the first time, he admitted to

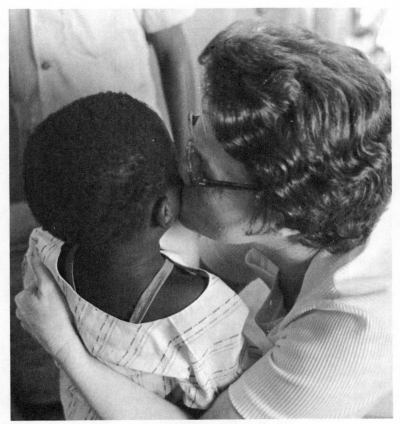

Missionary Marilyn Bonnell comforting a child at the immunization clinic of the Baptist center in Abomey, Benin

himself that he had changed a great deal. He still believed in the old ways, and he liked the simple, easy lifestyle of people in the village; but in some respects the people seemed backward. He silently thought of these factors as they walked back to Gomé.

Ayato could tell Zukono was deep in thought, but he suspected Zukono was worried more about divorcing Narie than adjusting to life in the village. "You're still a young man, Zukono. I don't want to tell you what to do, but Narie would probably not be happy here, and I doubt if she would leave

Dakar. Even though you may feel some obligation to the children, they are not Fon. You would be much happier, I believe, if you married another Fon woman and lived here in Benin, either at Gomé or Abomey. Think about it. I would be glad to help you arrange a marriage and to find work."

Never once did Ayato mention the shame that he and the other members of the family had felt when Zukono's "bad seed" caused the death of his first wife and Amasou's twin. He knew without saying that by fathering three children by Narie, Zukono had proven that his seed was not bad. It was not necessary to bring up the painful subject. He was subtle in hinting, however, that this was no longer considered a problem by assuring Zukono that he would help him arrange a marriage with a Fon bride.

Just before darkness fell, Zukono suggested that they rest for a minute. Ayato knew they had not walked far enough for Zukono to be tired. As they sat on a fallen tree beside the path, Zukono unwrapped a bundle he was carrying and showed his brother the purchases he had made earlier that day in the fetish market.

He told Ayato about the two *gbos* that Togbo had agreed to make for him—the pendant to help him win any argument he had with Jean-Marc and the carved human figure that could be used to make Ruth go insane.

Ayato approved of his brother's purchases and agreed that the two *gbos* used properly together might provide exactly the right combination of power to prevent Amasou's marriage to Ruth. "Even if Amasou is so headstrong that he does not accept your arguments, he would not want to marry Ruth if she becomes insane," Ayato said.

Ayato made another suggestion. "You recall, I'm sure, that I suggested that you contact my wife's cousin, Coffi Kadjo, in Cotonou about the possibility of finding a government job for Jean-Marc. Kadjo has a daughter of marriageable age who is a student at the *lycée*. She would make an excellent wife for Jean-Marc if you can persuade him to remain in Benin and if you can prevent this marriage with the Yoruba girl. If you would like for me to, I will include in my note to Kadjo the suggestion that he invite you and Jean-Marc to dinner at his home."

Zukono agreed immediately. Jean-Marc's chances of getting a government job would be greatly enhanced if he were betrothed or married to the daughter of the adjutant to the director of the civil service.

III

The way Philippe looked at him with such awe was embarrassing to Jean-Marc. He suspected that Philippe saw himself and his own dreams fulfilled in the life of Jean-Marc. It made Jean-Marc realize how blessed he had been. He had been able to attain a high level of education, had been able to travel throughout West Africa, and had been able to attend the Baptist School of Theology—three things very few West Africans could claim.

Philippe asked a hundred and one questions, constantly looking at Jean-Marc with wonderment in his eyes. What was it like to ride in a ship on the ocean? How did it feel to be seasick? How did the way of life in Dakar differ from life in Abomey? Were the courses at the school of theology difficult? Where did he live at the school? How did he meet Ruth? What was it like to kiss a Yoruba? How did he meet Pierre? Why did they decide to "drink the vodun" and become "best friends"? What were the nightmares like? Did he really plan to go to Timbuktu as a missionary? What was it like in Timbuktu?

On and on the questions poured in a never-ending stream. With each reply, Philippe's eyes seemed to brighten with more admiration and amazement.

Jean-Marc decided he needed to do something to counteract what seemed to be developing into a bad case of hero-worship. So he began to ask Philippe questions about his own life and experience. He discovered that Philippe, too, was a twin, and that his twin sister, like his own twin, was dead.

Like most young men, Philippe preferred life in the city over life in the village. As a Christian, he found the support of fellow believers in the city to be a source of spiritual strength unavailable in the village. In the city, also, he found an opportunity to get an education that did not exist in the village.

Jean-Marc had already noticed that a large number of students, all dressed in identical khaki uniforms, walked the streets of Abomey. Philippe proudly pointed out that the level of education in Abomey was one of the highest in the nation because the Fon people had placed a high priority on education—in the cities, at least.

As Philippe began to open up and talk about his own life, Jean-Marc asked him something that he had wanted to talk with someone about ever since he had crossed the border into Benin.

"What is it like to live under a Marxist-controlled government?" Jean-Marc asked.

Philippe shrugged and passed off the question as almost irrelevant. "I don't really know," he replied. "I don't see much difference in the lives of the people under the revolutionary regime than I did under the previous military rule."

Philippe thought that the new Marxist government was more stable than any of the previous military-run governments. Like most Fon, Philippe regretted that the new Marxist government had changed the name of the country from Dahomey to Benin back in 1975. But before the current government took over in 1972, there had been seven revolutions, military coups, or changes in government in Dahomey from 1960 until 1972. During the same period, the country had five constitutions and 11 presidents.

Realizing Philippe was more knowledgeable and intelligent than he at first had supposed, Jean-Marc pressed him for the reasons for the instability of the government. "Why had there been so many revolutions before?"

"I don't really know," replied Philippe. "But I've heard a lot of people say it is because of the desire of the Goun tribe to control the government, even though there are only about 150,000 Goun in Benin compared to about 700,000 Fon. But most of the Goun live in the Porto Novo and Cotonou area, where the capital is located, and they have a higher education level than the majority of the Fon, the Adja, and the Bariba. The Adja is the second largest tribe with about 225,000. The Bariba, most of whom are Muslim, live in the northern part of Benin and number about 150,000. But I don't know for sure if tribal differences have all that much to do with the instability of the government. I just don't know much about politics, and I don't really care. It doesn't seem to make much difference who is in control of the government."

Jean-Marc asked if Philippe had encountered any problems as a Christian.

"No, none at all," Philippe replied. "I think Pastor Bonnell has had some problems with government red tape getting permission to build his house and to help Dr. Tom Starkey build the new Baptist dental clinic over in Bohicon, but that's not because the government is Marxist in philosophy. It just takes a long time to get permission to build anything here in Benin. It always has—even before the government became Marxist."

Jean-Marc asked Philippe about the unusually large number of policemen and soldiers who drove down the streets of Abomey on motor scooters. "Why are there so many? Do they ever stop you from worshipping in freedom?"

"No, they are our friends," Philippe said. "One reason there are so many is that this is the government's way of providing jobs for the men. They are here to protect us from robbers and thieves."

Jean-Marc asked why there were so many banners hanging across the highways proclaiming revolutionary slogans. "On the way here from the border, I saw banners saying things like 'Power to the People' and 'Imperialism Out of the Country' and 'Death to the Imperialists' and 'The Revolution Continues.' Why does the government hang all those banners across the roads? What do they mean?"

"Nothing, really, to the common people," Philippe replied. "Most people don't pay any attention to them because the politics of the government just doesn't affect them personally."

Jean-Marc was vitally interested in Philippe's views, for he had surmised from his study in the *lycée* that Marxism was anti-Christian and that the government would be likely to oppose Christianity. But apparently it was different in Benin.

"Frankly, I think some of the government leaders here say they are Marxist when really they don't know anything about Marxism or care about it. They just think they can get more money with less control from the Russians and the Chinese than they can from the French or the Americans."

Jean-Marc chuckled to himself, for he had started out asking Philippe all those questions to shift the conversation away from himself to talking about Philippe. But in doing so, Jean-Marc learned far more about how the people felt about the government than he thought possible.

But Jean-Marc did not succeed in making Philippe think about himself instead of idolizing him. When they finally went to sleep that night, Philippe admired Jean-Marc even more. "He's so humble," Philippe thought. "With all his travel and education, he really wanted to know what I thought about the Marxist government here. He really made me feel my views are important."

IV

Jean-Marc was impressed with the warmth and openness of the people he met in Abomey. And no one was warmer or friendlier than Dutton Bonnell.

Obviously, Philippe loved Bonnell like a father. Philippe confided that sometimes the people called Bonnell *"Le Coeur Ouvert,"* the man with the open heart. "He loves the people so much," Philippe said.

Jean-Marc noticed that Bonnell had a gift for joking with people, making them feel at ease and spreading his enthusiasm and excitement for life with everyone he met. His only problem was that he spoke no Fon. Bonnell said he wanted to learn Fon, but he just hadn't had time.

Dutton and Marilyn Bonnell seemed especially to love the children. Bonnell also spent a lot of time giving first aid to people who had accidents but who could not afford to go to the only hospital in Abomey. Bonnell gave people what he called "tender, loving care."

"I could be happy in Abomey as a pastor," Jean-Marc thought one night as he was making final preparations for his sermon on Sunday morning.

The next day the Baptist center was packed with more than 150 people. "This is the biggest crowd we've ever had," Bonnell said with excitement. "I've never seen so many people jammed into the center before." Turning to Philippe, he asked why so many people had come this Sunday.

"The people who were here last Sunday have been talking all week, telling their friends in the market and in the villages about the young Fon named Jean-Marc who spoke at the center last week," Philippe replied. "They've come to hear the Fon *pasteur.*"

Jean-Marc was thrilled but humbled by the response. As the crowd sang and as the congregation bowed, Jean-Marc prayed as he had never prayed before for an outpouring of God's spirit and power. His prayers were answered because 19 people came forward when the invitation was given at the close of the service.

That afternoon Bonnell asked Jean-Marc to come to his house, for he wanted to talk to him. After the lengthy African-style greeting, Bonnell looked at Jean-Marc earnestly. "Jean-Marc, I've been praying for you for the last eight years and didn't know it," Bonnell said.

Somewhat startled, Jean-Marc asked what he meant. Bonnell told of prayers that God would call a Fon young man to the gospel ministry to plant his life in Abomey in order to reach the Fon people. "I've always expected God to call someone from my own congregation. But he hasn't done that. Instead, God has sent you. I've been praying about this all week, and I am convinced that God has led you here to become pastor of the Baptist Church of Abomey. I want you to pray about it, but I am convinced that God is leading you to us, and us to you. You can lead this congregation because you speak the language in such a powerful, moving way that

Children's assembly at the Baptist center in Abomey, Benin

the people respond as if God himself is speaking to them.''

Jean-Marc was flattered and overjoyed by Bonnell's tribute. He knew he could be happy there. But he was troubled deep down by his feeling that God had called him not to Abomey to preach to the Fon, but to Timbuktu to preach to the Songhai.

That night, for the first time in years, the nightmare of death recurred. Just as vividly as before, Jean-Marc relived in his dream the horrible death of his best friend, Pierre. His heart ached as those piercing brown eyes looked into his, and Pierre uttered his last words: "Promise me you will take the good news of the gospel to our people."

And just as he did that night two years ago, Jean-Marc awoke screaming. Philippe, sleeping on the mat in the same room, raced to Jean-Marc's side, asking what was wrong. With a troubled heart, Jean-Marc told him about the dream and Pierre's request.

"This afternoon, Pastor Bonnell asked me to consider coming to Abomey as pastor of the church here," Jean-Marc confided. "I really want to accept. I love the people here. I love the church. I love you and Pastor Bonnell. But I believe God has called me to be a missionary to Pierre's people in Timbuktu. And I'm afraid I would never be able to sleep again at night if I don't respond to that call."

After talking much of the night with Philippe, Jean-Marc left for Gomé the next morning. He hurried back to try to talk his father into leaving earlier than they planned. He wanted to return to Lomé as soon as possible. He feared that if he stayed any longer in Abomey, he might weaken and accept Bonnell's proposal.

Surprisingly, Zukono seemed to be ready to leave Gomé. He wanted to return to Abomey for market day once again but said he would leave Abomey for Cotonou the day after that. He told Jean-Marc they would spend the weekend with Coffi Kadjo. Jean-Marc was delighted. He had thought he couldn't talk his father into leaving Gomé for another two weeks.

CONFRONTATION IN COTONOU

I

Trudging down the narrow path, Zukono and Jean-Marc had little to say as they walked for the final time from Gomé to Abomey. Both seemed to be wrapped up in their own private thoughts.

In the bundle he carried on his head, Zukono had placed the two *gbos* made for him by Togbo, the chief priest, to help him with his arguments with Jean-Marc and to put a curse on Ruth that would cause her to go insane.

As always when he traveled, Zukono carried in his pants pocket the *gbo* Togbo made long ago to protect him on his journey to Dakar. The antelope horn protruded slightly from his pants pocket; but no matter how uncomfortable it was, Zukono had his "safe journey" *gbo* on his person when he traveled, not in his bundle of belongings. He sincerely believed the charm protected him from harm.

In his shirt pocket, Zukono carried two letters, neither of which he could read, but the content of which Ayato had told him. One was the letter of introduction to Coffi Kadjo recommending Jean-Marc for a government job and also proposing betrothal of Jean-Marc to Kadjo's daughter, Aimée. The second letter was from Ayato to Deacon Oke, answering in detail each of the questions Oke had asked concerning Zukono's family.

Ayato told Zukono that Deacon Oke had been crafty in the way he had phrased the questions. None of the questions called for any kind of answers that might indicate whether or not Ayato or his family approved of the marriage; they asked for specific facts about the family background. Ayato, however, concluded his response to Deacon Oke by flatly stating that as head of the clan, he did not approve of this marriage between Fon and Yoruba.

Jean-Marc was preoccupied with what to tell Bonnell. Ever

since the recurrence of the nightmare the night he had preached, Jean-Marc had felt a growing conviction that he could not become pastor of the Abomey church. He felt he *must* carry out his promise to Pierre. He wasn't sure that was what he *wanted* to do—only that it was what he *had* to do.

In Abomey, while Zukono went to the market to see his friends for one last time, Jean-Marc went to the Baptist Center. While he was there, Bonnell returned from Bohicon, where he had earlier that morning helped Tom Starkey finish unloading some building materials that had just arrived for the construction of a new dental clinic similar to the one Jean-Marc had visited in Bouaké, Ivory Coast. The dentist was in the early stages of construction of the clinic, having been delayed for almost nine months while he tried to get a building permit. Bonnell encouraged Jean-Marc to stop in Bohicon, 10 kilometers east of Abomey on the road to Cotonou, but Jean-Marc said he doubted there would be time.

Bonnell then asked if Jean-Marc thought he would be able to stop at the Baptist mission office in Cotonou to meet Charles Knight, the business manager of the Benin Baptist Mission. Jean-Marc said he would like very much to meet Knight and agreed to deliver an important letter to him, a letter Bonnell feared might be lost in the mail.

Then Bonnell asked the question Jean-Marc had been trying to answer. "Jean-Marc, I've been praying ever since we talked Sunday that God would convince you that you should accept the challenge to serve as pastor of the church here. How do you feel about it?"

"I have mixed feelings," Jean-Marc replied. "What I want to do is to say yes to you, but I cannot."

Then he told Bonnell about his nightmare and his conviction that this was God's way of telling him not to forsake his pledge to carry out Pierre's dying request.

Bonnell was disappointed—not surprised. Philippe had already told him about the nightmare.

As Jean-Marc said goodbye to Philippe and Bonnell, there was a prevailing sadness that Jean-Marc seldom experienced. Philippe looked as if he might burst into tears at any moment. Bonnell first clasped Jean-Marc's hand and then grabbed him in a big hug. "This is not goodbye."

True to his promise, Jean-Marc stopped to deliver the letter to Charles Knight after he and his father were settled with Ayato's relatives in Cotonou. Knight was naturally interested in Jean-Marc's story as they talked. Two other missionaries came into the office. The taller man was Dick LeMaster, who, Jean-Marc learned later, worked with the Yoruba in the Porto Novo area. The smaller man was Bob Couts, who worked with the Goun.

While LeMaster and Couts got acquainted with Jean-Marc, Knight read the letter from Dutton Bonnell. In the letter, Bonnell told Knight all about Jean-Marc's visit and the response of the people to his preaching in Fon. "I've done all I could to try to persuade Jean-Marc to come here as pastor of the Abomey church," Bonnell wrote to Knight. "Please pray with me that God will lead him back to us here in Abomey." In addition to the letter about Jean-Marc, Bonnell also enclosed a check in payment for some personal supplies that Knight had ordered for him from the United States.

After he finished reading the letter, Knight told Jean-Marc, Couts, and LeMaster what Bonnell had said. "You made quite an impression on Dutton," he said. "He told me he is convinced that you will return one day to Abomey as pastor."

The four men visited for almost an hour, asking Jean-Marc about his experiences and his sense of calling to the ministry. When Couts and LeMaster prepared to leave, they asked Jean-Marc if they could give him a ride anywhere. Jean-Marc, anxious not to make his father wait for him, asked if they would take him to the civil service headquarters, where he was to meet his father.

III

Zukono waited more than an hour in a corridor outside the office of the chief of staff of the *Service Civique*, waiting for his sister-in-law's cousin to come from a meeting. Finally,

Zukono was ushered into a small cubbyhole office just large enough for a desk and two chairs. About 15 minutes later a big, barrel-chested man with a slightly bald head and bushy mustache walked into the room with all the authority of a military general. He was Coffi Kadjo.

Zukono introduced himself as the brother of Ayato and said he had brought a letter from Kadjo's sister and her husband.

Motioning for Zukono to be seated in the chair, Kadjo opened the letter, sat down behind the desk, and began to read. Even after learning that Zukono was a relative, Kadjo maintained the official formality of a government official. He looked intently at Zukono and asked pointedly: "Tell me why you think that your son would make a good government worker."

"Amasou is a diligent, responsible worker," Zukono replied without hesitation. "He completed his *lycée* work in Dakar and has done advanced study in Lomé, Togo."

Zukono was careful not to mention that Jean-Marc was a student at the Baptist School of Theology in Lomé or that he wanted to become a missionary. He feared these negative factors might keep his son from getting a job.

"Amasou is also an excellent speaker and writer of reports. He speaks and writes not only Fon and French, but also speaks Wolof and Ewe; and he has been learning some Yoruba."

Kadja was still formal and noncommittal. "Is your son studying at the University of Benin in Lomé? What is his field of study?"

Zukono knew he could hide the truth no longer. "No, he is studying at the Baptist School of Theology in Lomé. He has the foolish idea that he wants to become a Christian pastor, but I have advised him, instead, to seek work with the government of Benin."

"I see," muttered Kadjo. "That must explain why Jean-Marc did not come with you today, and why you and Ayato are trying to arrange this job for him. He doesn't really want to work for the *Service Civique*, does he?"

Just as he asked the question, there was a knock at the door, and the clerk who had directed Zukono to Kadjo's office told them that Jean-Marc was outside in the hallway looking for his father. Kadjo invited him into the office, apologizing for the fact that there was no room in the small office for another chair.

"Your father tells me that you are a student at the Baptist School of Theology in Lomé," Kadjo said. "What are your plans after you finish your education?"

"Well, I first hope to marry a fine Yoruba girl, and eventually I hope that we will be able to travel to Timbuktu in Mali, where I want to establish a Baptist church."

Jean-Marc's announcement obviously took Kadjo by surprise. Neither the letter from Ayato nor the earlier conversation with Zukono had hinted that this was Jean-Marc's personal desire.

"I don't understand," Kadjo said. "Why would you want to be the leader of a *Christian* church and follow the God of the westerners? How can any educated African like yourself believe in the God of colonialists and imperialists? How can anyone who has lived under the domination and control of the French worship the God of the French? The French came here with the gun in one hand and the Bible in the other. They oppressed our people and established Catholic churches. Colonialism and the spread of Christianity went together. I don't see how you, as an educated African, can follow this God of colonialism and imperialism."

Jean-Marc did not want to get into an argument, but he disagreed. "I am not Catholic," he insisted, "but that's not the point. I am a Christian because I am convinced that Jesus Christ is the Son of God and that he is the only way to salvation. He offers true freedom to all people, no matter when they were born."

Jean-Marc then launched into a brief sermon, stating what he believed and why, concluding with his commitment to become a Christian missionary to the people of Timbuktu.

Kadjo asked Jean-Marc if his commitment to this God of the westerners had affected his view of Marxism. "The government of Benin is committed to Marxist-Leninist philosophy because we believe this is the best political system for the people," he declared. "There is no room here for the god of Western imperialism. I do not understand how any African can believe in the religion of the French people who oppressed the people of West Africa for centuries. Marxism, we are convinced, is the only way of the future for Africa, and there is no room under Marxism for religious sentimentality. Lenin said so truthfully that religion is the opiate of the people," Kadjo insisted.

It was not only what Kadjo said that disturbed Jean-Marc; it was his arrogant, authoritative way that offended him most. Why is he lecturing me? Jean-Marc wondered. What had gone on before that prompted this outburst?

Not caring what the consequences might be, Jean-Marc defended his faith. "Just because French colonialists did not live up to the full measure of the gospel does not mean the Christian religion is not good for Africans. I believe Jesus Christ is the one, true, complete revelation of God to man and the only way to salvation for sinful man. Marxism is not the way of the future for Africa, for Marxism does not call for a change in the hearts and lives of men. It seeks to change only the structures of society; but there can be no real and permanent change for good in society without first a change for good in the lives of men.

"Besides," Jean-Marc pointed out, "you condemn me for accepting the 'foreign' God of the westerners, while you, yourself, obviously have done the same thing by accepting Marxism. Marxism is just as 'foreign' to African cultures as Christianity is."

Kadjo obviously was furious because Jean-Marc had the audacity to argue with him. Standing abruptly, he handed the letter from Ayato back to Zukono and addressed them both.

"This conversation is ended. There is no room in the civil service for someone like your son, Zukono, and there is no room in my family for someone with his views. I am a busy man; I must return to more pressing duties. Goodbye."

FINDING THE WAY

"I've never been so humiliated in all my life," Zukono lashed out at Jean-Marc the moment they walked outside the door of the civil service headquarters building. "How could you do that to me?"

"He started it," Jean-Marc retorted. "From the moment I walked into the room, he started arguing and lecturing me. He did not even have the courtesy to greet me as the nephew of his sister's husband. I've never met such a brash, rude, discourteous man in my life."

As they walked down the streets of Cotonou, father and son argued intensely.

"You don't know what you've done," Zukono lamented. "If you had not said what you said, all that I've worked for and hoped for and dreamed for could have come true."

Zukono abruptly stopped, put his bundle down on the ground, and rummaged inside. "Wait a minute," he told Jean-Marc. "There's something here I want." He turned his back to Jean-Marc and quickly slid the small white goard containing the cat's heart around his neck. He knew an argument with Jean-Marc was about to take place, and he wanted to win this one. Three times he softly said aloud, *"yewome, yewome, yewome,"* activating the power of the *gbo* given him a few days earlier by the *voduno* of Gomé.

Zukono was so mad at Jean-Marc he was even tempted to get out the other *gbo* and make his son go insane for three days. It would be a fitting punishment for what he had done today.

Picking up his bundle again, Zukono continued his tongue-lashing. "Why did you have to say so much? You didn't have to argue with him. Why couldn't you have just kept your opinions to yourself?"

Jean-Marc decided that was exactly what he would do. He would simply not respond to his angry father. In silence they walked down the street, walking faster as if the faster they walked, the quicker they would solve their differences.

"I'm ready to go back to Lomé right now," Jean-Marc declared as he continued to seethe in anger. "You can go with me if you like, but I'm ready to go to the bus station and leave immediately. And whether you approve or not, and whether her parents and family approve or not, I intend to marry Ruth. I've made up my mind about another thing too, and you might as well know it. I intend to carry out my pledge to Pierre. As soon as possible, I am going to Timbuktu. I'm not even sure I will complete my study at the school of theology."

Buoyed by his faith in the *gbo*, Zukono decided it was time for a final, no-holds-barred argument with his son about his future.

"You can't be serious, Amasou," he insisted. "Be practical. How will you be able to support your wife, and your children when they are born, in a place like Timbuktu? How will you earn even enough money to feed yourself and your family in a part of the world where there is the constant threat and danger of famine and starvation? How will you start a church from scratch in an area of Muslim influence so strong that there is bound to be opposition to Christianity?"

Jean-Marc walked faster down the crowded street when Zukono started asking the tough questions he did not want to hear. Zukono quickened his step, thinking that his son was trying to avoid the questions by walking away from them.

"If God is calling me to Timbuktu, he will provide the way and the financial support," Jean-Marc insisted.

"Maybe that's the point," Zukono replied. "You said it yourself: 'If God is calling me to Timbuktu . . .' What if God is *not* calling you to Timbuktu, but you only think that he is because of your own guilt and grief that Pierre died and not you!"

Zukono smiled, for the *gbo* seemed to be working. Never had he felt so confident in arguing his points with his son. He seemed to be raising questions Jean-Marc could not answer.

Jean-Marc walked still faster. "Stop it!" he shouted. "I *know* God is calling me. I have no doubts."

His eyes flashing red with anger, Jean-Marc stepped off the curb and into the street without even looking, directly into the path of an oncoming truck.

Zukono shouted a warning and shoved his son with all his might. But the truck was on top of them both before they could get out of the way. Brakes squealed. Tires slid on the sandy pavement. Too late.

The left front fender of the truck hit Jean-Marc on the left leg, tossing his body like a match stick to the pavement. Knocked unconscious by the blow, Jean-Marc lay on the pavement while a crowd of onlookers gathered, calling for help.

It was too late to do anything for Zukono. He was dead. The front bumper hit him solidly, knocking his body to the pavement straight ahead. In the split second that followed, the heavy truck rolled over the limp form, instantly crushing life from Zukono's mangled body.

Around Zukono's neck was the *gbo* that worked, for he had won his argument with his son. But in his pocket was the *gbo* that failed. In a valiant effort to save his son, Zukono had lost his life.

II

It was several hours before Jean-Marc regained consciousness. When he awoke, he found himself in a small hospital room in Cotonou with three other patients.

At his side were Bob Couts and Dick LeMaster, who chanced across the accident shortly after they started back to Porto Novo after completing their business in Cotonou.

"How is my father?" Jean-Marc asked, already knowing the answer in his heart.

"There was no hope for him," LeMaster replied softly and tenderly. "He died instantly."

Big tears welled up in Jean-Marc's eyes and overflowed down his black cheeks. "Why, God? That's twice that someone I love died so that I might live! Why?" he sobbed.

Couts walked to Jean-Marc's side and took his hand. "Not

twice, but three times," he whispered. "Jesus, too, died that you might live. You ask why? Because they all loved you so much they were willing to give up their own lives so that you might live. There is no greater love than that, Jean-Marc!"

By then, tears were streaming down the cheeks of the missionaries too.

As LeMaster came to the side of the bed and the three men held hands, Couts voiced the feelings of each: "God, we praise your name because you love us so that you gave your only Son that we might have life eternal. And we praise your name that two people loved Jean-Marc so much that they, too, were willing to die that he might live. We don't understand why they had to die, Lord. But we know that Jean-Marc loved them too, and that he would as willingly have given up his life for them. And even if we don't understand death and suffering, we know that you can take this tragic accident and somehow bring about good from it.

"Thank you, Lord, for Jean-Marc. We commit his life to you, knowing that you will use him in a powerful way. Comfort him in his grief. Give him understanding. Give him the peace that passes all understanding. And we will give you all the praise and glory and honor because we ask this in the name of Jesus, and for his sake. Amen."

Jean-Marc sobbed unashamedly. Couts had expressed in words so beautiful what he felt deep inside but could not bring himself to say. With Couts and LeMaster by his side, continuing to pray silently, Jean-Marc soon began to get control of his emotions. In a few moments, his practical nature once again surfaced.

"I will need to make arrangements for my father's burial and funeral," he said. "How long will I have to be in the hospital?"

"The doctor came by earlier," replied LeMaster. "He said you would have to be here at least three weeks. You have a broken leg. You'll have to wear a cast for about three months and walk only on crutches for maybe as long as six months. But don't worry about the funeral arrangements. We will be glad to help you."

"My father was not a Christian," Jean-Marc lamented. "He would want to be buried in his hometown village of Gomé, according to the traditions of our people. Is there any way you can notify my father's brother in Gomé of his death? His name is Ayato, and he is the village chief there. It is a small village about 15 kilometers from Abomey, and there are no telephones.

Couts suggested that they telephone Dutton Bonnell immediately and ask Bonnell to go to the village and notify Ayato. They would work out the arrangements for shipping Zukono's body back to Gomé for the burial and funeral.

"Is there anything else we can do for you?" LeMaster asked.

"There is one other thing, but I hate to ask you to do it," Jean-Marc replied. "Could you send a cable to Lomé, to Ruth, the girl I love, and tell her what has happened? Ask her if there is any way she can come to be with me during these next few days."

Couts and LeMaster agreed to help in all these ways, and after another word of prayer, they left to take care of the necessary details.

III

Jean-Marc wept tears of joy, not grief, when the door opened and Ruth walked into his hospital room. Even though the three other patients remained in the small room, he wept unashamedly as she rushed to his bedside. Ruth's eyes told Jean-Marc that she shared his grief as she took his hand and held it to her cheek.

In hushed whispers, they told each other how much they loved one another and how much they had missed being together. The quarrel of that last night together seemed to be forgotten.

Ruth picked up Jean-Marc's Bible that lay on the bed. Taking his hand again, she began to read from the book of the Bible that bore her own name, the first chapter, verses 16-17:

"And Ruth said, Entreat me not to leave thee, or to return

from following after thee: for whither thou goest, I will go; and where thou lodgest, I will lodge: thy people shall be my people, and thy God my God: Where thou diest, will I die, and there will I be buried: the Lord do so to me, and more also, if aught but death part thee and me."

"Jean-Marc," she said. "That is the message that God has given me to share with you. No matter where you go, no matter what you feel God is leading you to do, I want to be by your side—even if it means going to Timbuktu."

"I don't know where God is leading me yet," Jean-Marc replied. "But I do know that he has led us together. And wherever he leads us in the future, we will remain together.

"Since the accident," he continued, "I've had time to think, to pray, and to read God's word. The thing that has disturbed me most is why it was my father, not I, who was killed, when I was never able to lead him to Christ. I don't know what God is trying to teach me through this experience, but I know there is something for me to learn from it. Let's pray together that I will understand his redemptive purpose and that he will reveal his plan for us."

Ruth knelt at Jean-Marc's bedside; holding hands, they prayed that God would guide them in the future and help them to find his will for their lives together. And as they prayed, a peace and tranquillity settled over them like mist on thirsty grass.

IV

That night Jean-Marc awoke the whole hospital ward with his screams. It was the nightmare again, the second time in the last two weeks. In vivid technicolor, Jean-Marc relived the death of his best friend and heard those same haunting words.

For the rest of the night he lay awake, praying and thinking. Why was he so torn apart by the terrible, recurring nightmare? Why had the dreams started again?

Suddenly it dawned on him. Jean-Marc remembered a conversation between him and Pierre soon after Pierre started going to the Baptist center regularly. The words of the dream took on new meaning.

When Pierre whispered those last words, he had said, "Promise me you will take the good news of the gospel to our people." He didn't say *my* people; he said *our* people!

As clearly as if the conversation had taken place that morning, Jean-Marc remembered something Pierre said one day as they were walking home from the *lycée.*

"You know, Jean-Marc," Pierre had said that afternoon, "I've come to the point that I look at myself more as an African than just as a Songhai. Being your friend and knowing Pastor Runyan caused that. There is really no difference in people of other tribes and other races.

"What I really want to be able to do," he continued, "is some day to see the whole world the way Jesus sees it. Obviously, I cannot ever completely see the *whole* world the way Jesus does; but I pray I can just see Africa, or even West Africa, with the eyes of Jesus. Jesus has a concern not only for the Songhai and the Fon, but for the people of every tribe, every tongue, every nation, every race."

Suddenly Jean-Marc understood Pierre's last words from a new perspective. Maybe, he thought, God was trying to tell him that he should proclaim the gospel, not just to the Songhai of Timbuktu, but to all the people of West Africa— yes, even all of Africa and the whole world!

In a flash, the experiences of the past two years passed before his eyes. Into his mind came the images of the people he had come in contact with all across West Africa. He thought of the people of Ivory Coast and the starving people of Koudougou and Tenkoudougou. He thought of the villagers in Ewe-speaking towns of Togo, where he came to know the joy of preaching. He remembered his burning desire to help the Muslims of Dakar to understand that Christ is truly the Son of God. He recalled most vividly the thrill of preaching in his native language to the Fon of Abomey and the excitement of seeing 19 people accept Christ in one morning.

In a flood of revelation, Jean-Marc realized that "the way"

to Timbuktu is through *all* of French-speaking West Africa. He realized that his calling was not a narrow, geographic, tribal call to proclaim the gospel only to the Songhai people of one city. Instead, it was the call to proclaim the gospel to *all* "our people."

And that meant he should start right there—in a hospital in Cotonou, Benin. To everyone he met, he would proclaim Jesus as "the way, the truth, and the life."

And if "the way" led him eventually to Timbuktu, fine. But Jean-Marc knew that the one who had led him thus far in his pilgrimage of faith would guide him in the future, if he remained faithful in the present.

ABOUT THE AUTHOR

Jim Newton is news editor of the Home Mission Board. Before assuming that position in 1980, he was editor of *World Mission Journal* and director of the Editorial Department, Baptist Men's Division, of the Brotherhood Commission for seven years.

A native of Texas and a graduate of Baylor University, Newton began his career in denominational journalism as press representative for the Baptist General Convention of Texas. He was assistant director of Baptist Press for eight years before joining the staff of the Brotherhood Commission.

Newton's news coverage has taken him to South America, Europe, Africa, and Asia. During his career he has won 27 awards in the Baptist Public Relations Association and the Religious Public Relations Council.

He and his wife, Pat, have two daughters, Jana and Kayla.

PRONUNCIATION OF SIGNIFICANT WORDS

PART ONE

Dakar—dah-KAR
Amasou—ah-mah-soo
Jean-Marc—zhahn-mark
Wolof—wuh-luhf
lycée—lee-say
Zukono—z'ue-koh-noh
fa—fah
Narie—nah-REE
Sonni Bakari—soh-nee BAH-kah-ree
Songhai—song-eye
Peul—p'uhl
Sunni—soo-nee
toubob—too-bob
Gou—goo
Agé—ah-zhay
Liberté—LEE-bear-tay
Route de la Corniche—root duh lah
  kor-NEESH
quartier—CAR-tee-ay
Centre Baptiste—SAHN-truh bah-TEEST
Sékou Diatta—say-koo d'yah-tah
pasteur—pahs-TER
A la Découverte de la Bible—ah lah
  DAY-coo-vairt duh lah BEE-bluh

Denis—duh-NEE
Le Merveilleux Plan de Dieu—luh
  MAIR-vay-yur plahn duh d'yew
Qui Est Jésus—kee ay ZHAY-zu
Principes Fondamentaux de
  l'Enseignement Biblique—prah-seep
  FAW-dah-mahn-toh duh
  LAH-sahn-yuh-mahn bee-bleek
étudier—AY-tyew-d'yay
s'appliquer—SAH-plee-kay
collège—koh-LEHZH
Ouagou Niayes—wah-guh n'yeye
Boulevard du Général de Gaulle—
  BOOL-var du ZHAY-nay-rahl duh gohl
Lomé—loh-MAY
Casamance—KAH-sah-mahns

PART TWO

Esprit de Liberté—ess-pree duh
  LEE-bear-tay
Baoulé—BAH-oo-lay
Gorée—goh-ray
Ebrié—AY-bree-ay
Boulay—boo-lay

Bai du Banco—bay dyew BAHN-koh
Treichville—TRESH-veel
Marcory—MAR-koh-ree
Tam Tam—tahm tahm
Baie de Cocody—bay duh KOH-koh-dee
Hôtel Ivoire—oh-tel ee-vwar
Yopougon—YOH-poo-gohn
Dion Robert—d'yohn roh-BEAR
Bouaké—bwah-kay
d'Atakpamé—dah-tahk-PAH-may
Sitobo Yosoufou—SEE-toh-boh
 YOH-soo-foo
guardien—gar-d'yann
Ewe—eh-veh
Foyer Baptiste—fwah-yeh bah-TEEST
Cocoteraie—KOH-koh-t'ray
Sokodé—SOH-koh-day
Oke Isaac—o-keh ee-zak
Adejumo—ah-DAY-joo-moh
Ibiyemi—ee-bee-yeh-mee
Abidjan—AH-bee-djahn
Cotonou—KOH-toh-noo
Akakpo Vizah Millissor—AH-kahk-poh
 vee-zah mee-lee-sor
mille kilos—meel KEE-low

Koudougou—KOO-doo-goo
Ouagadougou—wah-gah-DOO-goo
Tenkoudougou—ten-KOO-doo-goo
Iwo—ee-WOH
République—RAY-pyew-bleek
Place de l'Indépendance—plahss duh
 lan-day-pahn-dahns
Bobo-Dioulasso—boh-boh-d'you-LAH-
 soh

PART THREE
Bokono—BOH-koh-noh
Ouidah—wee-dah
Abomey—AH-boh-may
Grimo—gree-moh
gare—gar
Tchiméoudou Philippe—
 chee-AY-moo-doo fee-LEEP
Ayato—AH-yah-toh
Tosu—toh-zue
Dosu Togbo—doh-zue toh-gboh
Service Civique—sair-veece see-veek
Le Coeur Ouvert—luh kur oo-vair

PERSONAL LEARNING ACTIVITIES

1. List at least three handicaps faced by young people in French-speaking West Africa when they convert to Christianity. Explain them by referring to characters in the novel.

2. Why is a university education for their children so important to parents in this area?

3. Describe two ways the Baptist center in Dakar, Senegal, ministers to the needs of young people.

4. Discuss the different kinds of training available to Christians in French-speaking West Africa in addition to the theological school at Lomé.

5. Why is it more difficult for a new believer in this area to become an evangelical Christian than to become a Catholic?

6. List at least three different ways Southern Baptist missionaries are found ministering to Africans in the novel.

7. Compare and contrast the way young Africans in the novel and people in this country approach marriage.

8. Mention two reasons for understandably negative feelings Africans might have toward white westerners.

9. Give and explain two reasons why "number of converts" is not a fair way to measure the effectiveness of mission outreach in French-speaking West Africa.

10. What truth about the way Jesus views the world does the main character understand at the close of the story?

APPROPRIATE RESPONSES TO A STUDY OF MISSIONS

My commitment: to the best of my ability and with God's help I will

(   ) **Pray for missions and missionaries.**
For a prayer list and missions information refer to *The Commission, Open Windows, World Mission Journal, Probe, Royal Service, Contempo, Accent.*

(   ) **Give to the annual Lottie Moon Christmas Offering for Foreign Missions, through my local church.**

(   ) **Keep up with current foreign mission news.**
Subscribe to *The Commission* and magazines listed above.

(   ) **Accept the call of God to become a missionary.**
For further information write to: Foreign Mission Board, Box 6597, Richmond, Virginia 23230.

(   ) **Serve from two weeks to two years on a mission field as a volunteer.**
Write to the Foreign Mission Board, Box 6597, Richmond, Virginia 23230 for information about volunteer opportunities.

(   ) **Encourage my church to increase our Cooperative Program giving.**

(   ) **Include foreign missions in my will.**
For further information write to: Foreign Mission Board Treasurer, Box 6597, Richmond, Virginia 23230.

Signed _____ Date _____

(Keep this commitment record as a reminder.)

The Church Study Course

The Church Study Course consists of a variety of short-term credit courses for adults and youth and noncredit foundational units for children and preschoolers. The materials are for use in addition to the study and training curriculums made available to the churches on an ongoing basis.

Study courses and foundational units are organized into a system that is promoted by the Sunday School Board, 127 Ninth Avenue, North, Nashville, Tennessee 37234; by the Woman's Missionary Union, 600 North Twentieth Street, Birmingham, Alabama 35203; by the Brotherhood Commission, 1548 Poplar Avenue, Memphis, Tennessee 38104; and by the respective departments of the state conventions affiliated with the Southern Baptist Convention.

Study course materials are flexible enough to be adapted to the needs of any Baptist church. The resources are published in several different formats—textbooks of various sizes, workbooks, and kits. Each item contains a brief explanation of the Church Study Course.

Types of Study and Credit
Adults and youth can earn study course credit through individual or group study. Teachers of courses or of foundational units are eligible to receive credit.

1. Class Experience.—Group involvement with course material for the designed number of hours for the particular course. Study course credit requirements call for a person to read, view, or listen to the course material and to attend class sessions. A person who is absent

from one or more sessions must complete the "Personal Learning Activities" or other requirements for the material missed.

2. Individual Study.—This includes reading, viewing, or listening to course material and completing the specified requirements for the course.

3. Lesson Course Study.—Parallel use of designated study course material during the study of selected units in Church Program Organization periodical curriculum units. Guidance for credit appears in the selected periodical.

4. Institutional Study.—Parallel use of designated study course material during regular courses at educational institutions, including Seminary Extension Department courses. Guidance for this means of credit is provided by the teacher.

Credit is awarded for the successful completion of a course of study. This credit is granted by the Church Study Course Awards Office, 127 Ninth Avenue, North, Nashville, Tennessee 37234, for the participating agencies. Credit may be requested on the coupon in the book, or Form 151. "Church Study Course Credit Request, Revised 1975."

When credit is issued to a person on request, the Awards Office sends two copies of a notice of credit earned to the church. The duplicate copy of the credit slip should be filed by the study course clerk in the participant's record of training folder. The original should be given to the person who earned the credit. Accumulated credits are applied toward a specific leadership diploma or the Christian Development Diplomas, which are measures of learning, growth, development, and training.

Detailed information about the Church Study Course system of credits, diplomas, and record keeping is available from the participating agencies. Study course materials, supplementary teaching or learning aids, and forms for record keeping may be ordered from Baptist Book Stores.

The Church Study Course Curriculum
Credit is granted on those courses listed in the current copy of *Church Materials Catalog,* and *Church Study Course Catalog.* When selecting

courses or foundational units, the current catalogs should be checked to determine what study course materials are valid.

How to Request Credit for this Course

This book is the text for a course in the subject area: Missions.

This course is designed for 2½ hours of group study. Credit is awarded for attending class sessions and reading the book. A person who is absent from one or more class sessions must complete the "Personal Learning Activities" for the material missed.

Credit is also allowed for use of this material in individual study. A person desiring credit for an individual study should read this book and complete the "Personal Learning Activities."

Credit for this study can be applied to one or more diplomas in the Church Study Course.

After the course is completed, the teacher, the study course clerk, the learner, or any person designated by the church should complete Form 151 (Church Study Course Credit Request, Revised 1975) and send it to the Awards Office, 127 Ninth Avenue, North, Nashville, Tennessee 37234. In the back of this book the reader will find a form which he may cut out, fill in, and send to the Awards Office for credit.